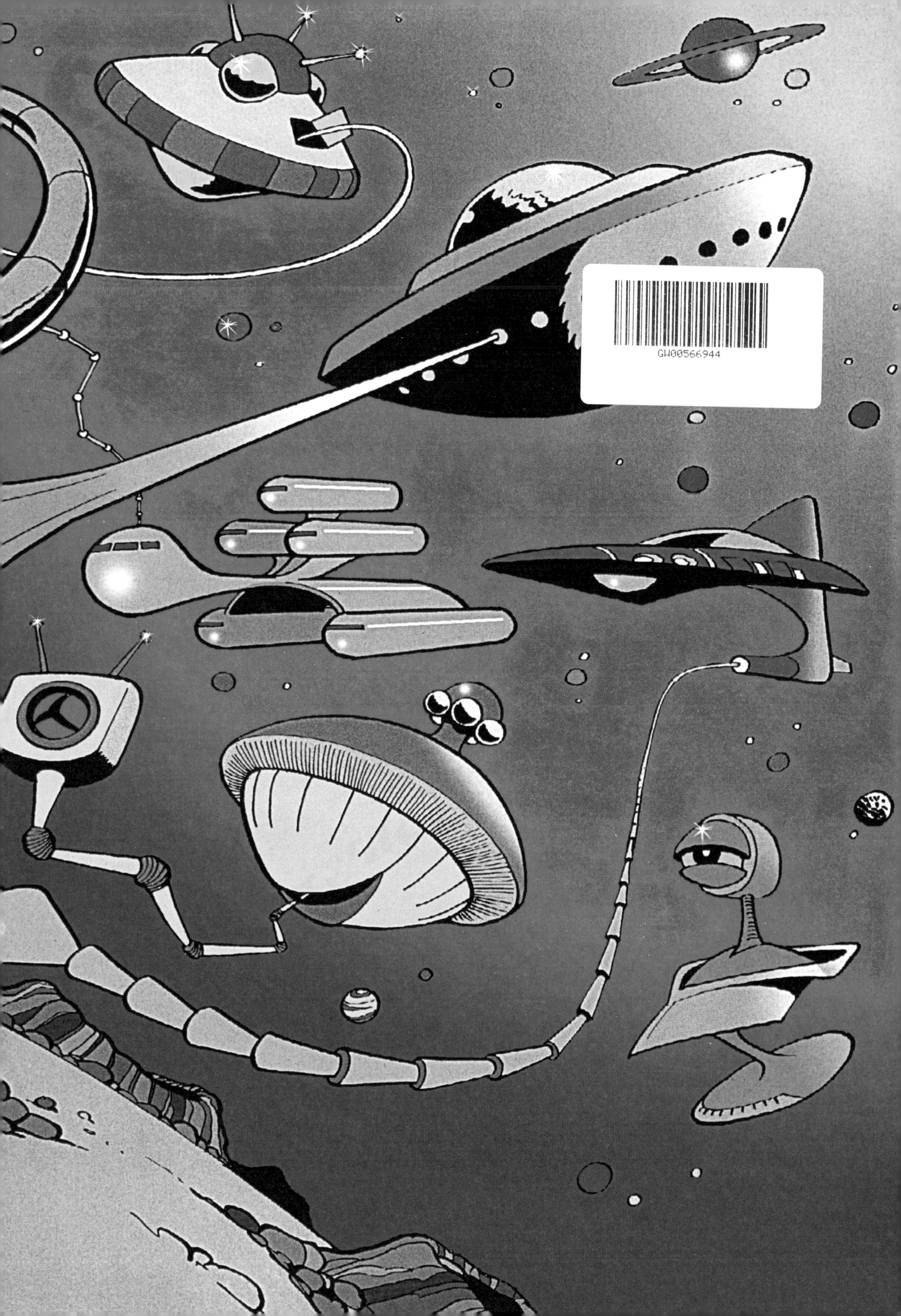
GW00566944

FIRST AID
TAXI
M

Enter, test subjects! Come into our laboratory of laughs!

Put down that beaker of mystery liquid and pick up a comic as The Dandy and Beano teach us a thing or two about the appliance of science! Observe inside these pages a methodology of madness from DC Thomson's archives for you to study! This astronomical anthology features classic strips from Dennis the Menace, Desperate Dan and Minnie the Minx, together with experimental whizzes like Rubi von Screwtop, Brassneck, General Jumbo and even more maniacs than we could name!

This encyclopaedia of bubbling beakers, devious devices, and impish inventions is not only your study guide to mayhem, as contained within its pages is some of the most atomic artwork from some of Britain's top comics artists, whose inventive illustrations are laid out in the lab ready for you!

Printed in Italy.

Some pages may contain references which are of their time, but would not be considered suitable today.

THE HORSE THAT JACK BUILT

ON a broad stretch of green grass near a village in Merrie England, a tournament was in progress. The Black Baron, who owned the lands for miles around, was challenging all-comers to mounted combat. And there was only one bold enough to accept the challenge—little Jack Pratt, son of Cedric the Toymaker.

2—The villagers shivered in their shoes as they heard Jack accept the challenge, for the Baron was a cruel tyrant, and Jack was only a young boy. The Baron hooted with laughter as he watched Jack race into the nearby forest. "I'll teach that insolent pup when he returns!" he boasted. "Make ready for the combat!"

Who will fight the fierce Black Knight?

3—Meanwhile Jack had reached a cave deep in the forest. There he lived with his parents, helping his father, who was the cleverest toymaker in the whole wide world. Quickly Jack told his father of the Baron's challenge. " You will need the Clockwork Horse !" exclaimed Cedric. " Come. We will arrange a few surprises for the boastful Baron !" And the pair set to work.

4—Inside the cave stood a beautiful clockwork horse. It was the most marvellous steed in the world, for it could run and jump like a real horse. For an hour Cedric worked on the horse, and when he was finished, Jack mounted and rode like the wind back to the tournament. He was ready now to meet the Baron's challenge.

One minute Jack's there—

5—News of the strange contest quickly spread among the crowd, and they packed the rail round the tilting ground. Armed with long lances, Jack and the big Baron cantered to opposite ends of the lists, then turned and galloped their mounts towards each other! The crowd watched in horror, quite sure that Jack was riding to his death.

6—But Jack and his father had not wasted their time in the cave. They had made several clever alterations to the Clockwork Horse, and now, as the Baron thundered towards him, Jack reached for a lever behind his saddle. Holding his long lance steady in front, he pulled the lever hard over. The Black Baron was in for a shock!

—The next—THIN AIR!

7—By now the two galloping steeds were within thirty paces of each other, and, with a roar of triumph, the Baron aimed his lance. But strange things were happening to the Clockwork Horse ! Its tube-like legs were growing longer. Each leg was extending like a giant telescope, lifting Jack higher and higher off the ground.

8—As the Black Baron gave a mighty thrust with his lance, the legs of the Clockwork Horse shot out to three or four times their normal length, and Jack was carried up well clear of danger. The astounded Baron, unable to check his horse, found himself galloping through between the gigantic steel legs of Jack's mechanical steed !

See Jack rise—

9—In a split second it was all over, and the wonderful Clockwork Horse galloped clear, thundering down the lists with enormous strides. But the Baron was not so fortunate. His lance-point, missing its target, plunged into the ground, and he found himself jerked from his saddle and landing with a terrific clatter on his back.

10—Quickly Jack pulled the lever back, and the Clockwork Horse's legs returned to normal size. As the Black Baron staggered to his feet, drawing his sword as he did so, young Jack cantered up, ready to end the fight peacefully. But the Baron had not finished. With a bellow of anger he swung his sword, and it fairly whistled through the air.

—And win the prize.

11—But Jack had another trick up his sleeve. At a touch of a hidden button, the saddle of the Clockwork Horse shot up on a cunningly-hidden set of expanding steel rods. The Baron's sword whistled harmlessly beneath Jack's feet, and the tyrant overbalanced, to fall with a crash on his back. In a twinkling, Jack lowered his saddle again and thrust with his lance.

12—The sharp tip of the lance was held against the Baron's throat, and the contest was over. The tyrant had to confess himself beaten. As a cheer rose from the crowd, Jack dropped his lance and grabbed the Baron's black-plumed helmet. Next minute he was galloping home with a grand souvenir of his victory over the Black Baron !

JAMES' SCIENCE PROJECTS

The MOVING ISLAND

Young Mickey Martin had lived all his life by the sea, and had a rowing boat which was all his own. One Saturday morning, Captain Mickey and Chips, his tough little terrier pal, got under way to go fishing. The sea was calm and the day started off like any other Saturday.

WHAT ABOUT MY ROWING BOAT? IT'S LOST BACK THERE SOMEWHERE!
WE'LL GO AND LOOK FOR IT, MICKEY!

ARE YOU ENJOYING YOURSELF?
SUPER! THIS IS THE LIFE!

PROFESSOR! THERE'S SOMETHING WRONG WITH THE ENGINE!
CLANK! WHIRR! CLANK!

IT WON'T TAKE ME LONG TO FIX IT!
OKAY, PROFESSOR- I WON'T TOUCH ANY BUTTONS THIS TIME!

THERE'S THAT ISLAND WE WERE ORDERED TO LOOK FOR. STAND BY FOR'ARD!
TARGET BEARING RED ZERO THREE ZERO...
THAT MERCHANT SHIP REPORTED IT WAS A DANGER TO SHIPPING. WE'D BETTER DESTROY IT!

FIRE!

THE PROFESSOR HAD JUST FINISHED REPAIRING THE ENGINE WHEN THE FIRST SALVO LANDED.
WOW! WE'RE BEING SHELLED! LET'S GET MOVING!
HEY! WE'RE HERE!

IT'S NO GOOD, PROFESSOR- WE CAN'T ESCAPE!
DON'T WORRY, MICKEY-I'VE GOT SOMETHING UP MY SLEEVE...

I HOPE IT FOOLS THEM!
...A SMOKESCREEN!

CEASE FIRE! IT LOOKS LIKE A DIRECT HIT!

YOU'RE A GENIUS, PROFESSOR!
WE'LL BE GONE WHEN THE SMOKE CLEARS, AND THEY'LL THINK THEY'VE SUNK US!

IT WASN'T LONG BEFORE THE PALS RAN INTO A NEW ADVENTURE!
WE'VE HIT SOMETHING!

IT'S A WHALE!

CRASH!

CAN'T YOU STOP IT SPINNING, PROFESSOR?
NO! IT'S OUT OF CONTROL! HANG ON, MICKEY!

THE WHALE JAMMED SOMETHING WHEN IT HIT US! WE'RE RUNNING AWAY!

ICEBERGS! POLAR BEARS! WHAT NEXT?

IT WAS HOURS BEFORE THE PROFESSOR REGAINED CONTROL OF THE ISLAND.
EVERYTHING'S OKAY NOW!
I THOUGHT WE WERE GOING TO END UP AT THE NORTH POLE! I'M FREEZING!

WE'RE LOST, MICKEY, BUT DON'T WORRY-WE'LL GET OUR COURSE HOME FROM THAT WEATHER SHIP!

WE PICKED UP A MESSAGE ABOUT A MOVING ISLAND BUT WE THOUGHT IT WAS JUST A HOAX!
YOUR MOTHER'LL HAVE SOMETHING TO SAY ABOUT THIS, SON!

ON THE WAY BACK.
WE'RE WELL ON OUR WAY NOW-BUT THERE'S A STORM COMING UP!

DON'T WORRY, MICKEY-THE ISLAND'S AS SAFE AS ANY SHIP!

FOUR HOURS LATER - THE CHUMS SIGHT A SHIP IN DISTRESS.
THAT TRAWLER'S IN DIFFICULTIES! LOOK! THEY'RE ASKING OUR HELP!

THE TRAWLER WAS SINKING, AND ONE OF THE CREW WAS BADLY INJURED.

THE PROFESSOR REVEALED MORE OF THE AMAZING ISLAND'S SECRETS....
I GAN GIVE YOU A LIGHT TO WORK BY, CAPTAIN!
-AND A FIRST AID KIT! THAT'S GREAT, PROFESSOR!

THIS MAN'S IN A BAD WAY. WE'LL HAVE TO GET HIM TO HOSPITAL!

THE ISLAND SAILED SOUTHWARDS ALL THAT NIGHT, AND WHEN MORNING DAWNED-
WE CAN HEAD ACROSS COUNTRY TO THE HOSPITAL!

HOSPITAL
I CAN'T THANK YOU ENOUGH, PROFESSOR! YOU'VE SAVED ALL OUR LIVES!
ROBERTSC

THE ISLAND'S NEXT JOURNEY WAS BACK TO THE COAST, TO THE TOWN WHERE MICKEY LIVED.
WHERE HAVE YOU BEEN, MICKEY?
YOU'LL FIND OUT IN THE EVENING PAPERS, DAD!

AND, A FEW DAYS LATER-
IT'S FOR YOU, MICKEY- A PRESENT FROM THE PROFESSOR! HE SAYS IT'S TO REPLACE THE ONE YOU LOST THE OTHER DAY.
ISLAND CHIEFTAIN
GOLLY! THAT PROFESSOR'S A REAL TOFF!

THE BASH STREET KIDS

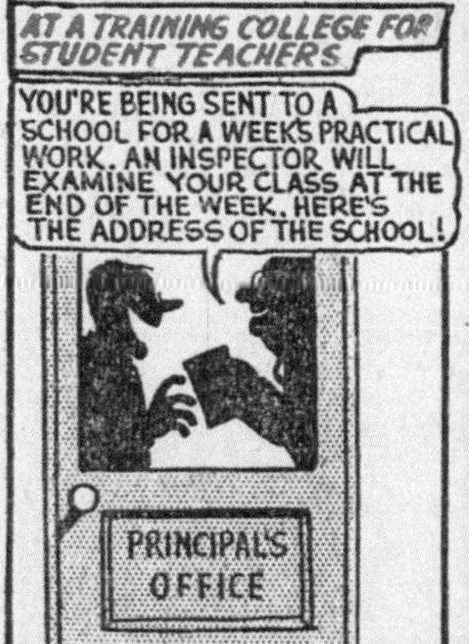

GENERAL JUMBO

General Jumbo's Army was on parade! On a stretch of waste ground, Jumbo Johnson was drilling his model soldiers and tanks, watched by a bunch of thrilled youngsters. Jumbo was grinning happily as he twiddled the buttons on the marvellous "box of tricks" that controlled the models by radio waves. The models were the work of Professor Carter, a brilliant scientist whose life Jumbo had once saved. As a reward, the Prof had allowed Jumbo to take charge of his models. The models were kept in a special van which was now parked nearby, while the Prof called on a friend.

Wham! Jumbo gave a gasp of dismay as a football crashed into the line of tiny soldiers, badly damaging several of them. "Get them toys out of the way, kid!" bawled Mugsy Miller, the bully who had kicked the ball. "Then clear off yourself! You're on our pitch!"

The rest of the youngsters started to protest, but they were no match for the toughs. "Hurry up an' shove off!" growled another of the louts, roughly cuffing one of the lads aside. There was a grim look on Jumbo's usually merry face. The General was about to go into action!

One of the toughs misjudged a header, and sent the football spinning into a patch of long grass. Jumbo pressed a couple of buttons to send a model tank speeding down the ramp leading from the van. The tank was closely followed by four soldiers. The models headed for the long grass.

The tank flattened out a path through the grass which the tiny soldiers followed. After a bit of juggling with the controls, the boy succeeded in getting the models to raise the ball above their heads. Then the soldiers carried the football further away from the searching players.

Jumbo chuckled as he watched the puzzled toughs searching for their lost ball. They were baffled—it just didn't occur to them that it had been taken away by Jumbo's wonder models. The tough lads thought that the soldiers they had knocked over were toys—but they had another think coming!

Three model helicopters, with tiny hooks dangling underneath them, took off. One of the louts gave a yell as he felt a hook catching into his jacket collar. The toughs were so amazed that they put up almost no resistance as the powerful little helicopters dragged them towards a nearby pond!

When the toughs realised that they were going to end up in the water, they tried to draw back, but Jumbo pressed a switch, and the 'copters released the lines which held the hooks. Splash! Howling protests, the toughs toppled one by one into the icy water!

"It was that nipper with the fancy cap that did it!" spluttered Mugsy. "C'mon, let's—awk!" The toughs' leader broke off in alarm as General Jumbo's jets sped towards the pond. In the lead was the sinister bat-like shape of a Delta-winged bomber.

Really frightened this time, Mugsy led the toughs in a mad rush for their truck. With the tiny bombers close behind them, the three tough lads could certainly move! The model jets zoomed at low level over the toughs to score several direct hits with their loads of soot bombs.

With a crash of gears, the truck lurched into motion. As it went, Jumbo sent in his fighters! Howls of pain drifted back to the watching youngsters as the fighters' pea-shooters delivered their stinging blows. "On with the parade, lads," Jumbo grinned. "They won't bother us again!"

PRINCE WHOOPEE
YOUR PAL FROM THE PALACE
IT'S TIME YOU LEARNT HOW TO USE A SWORD, WHOOPEE! THIS IS YOUR FENCING-MASTER.
BAH! MORE LESSONS.
CHOOSE YOUR WEAPON, SIRE!

PAY CLOSE ATTENTION, SIRE! IT'S MOST USEFUL TO KNOW HOW TO DO THIS!
SWISH
SWISH
SLASH
CARRY ON AS YOU'RE DOING—MY PENCIL'S ALMOST SHARPENED NOW!

THIS IS ANOTHER USEFUL STROKE!
HA! HA! HA!
WOW!

GO AND PRACTISE YOUR SWORD PLAY—AND NO SLACKING!
AND REMEMBER, SIRE, THAT A FORWARD THRUST IS MOST USEFUL!

SO WHOOPEE GOES TO PRACTISE HIS SWORD PLAY....
PALACE KITCHE
H'M! THAT FORWARD THRUST IS GOING TO BE PRETTY USEFUL AFTER ALL!

R-R-R-RING
LIKE THIS!

PALACE KITCHE
I COULD SWEAR SOMEBODY RANG THE BELL!

AND WHILE THE COOK IS AT THE DOOR.
AND THIS!
I NEVER KNEW FENCING COULD BE SO INTERESTING!

I ENJOYED THAT! NOW FOR SOME MORE FUN!
ELECTRICITY DEPARTMENT

INSIDE THE ELECTRICITY DEPARTMENT.
JUST WHAT I'M LOOKING FOR!
ELECTRIC SHOCK MACHINE

SOON IT'S TIME FOR WHOOPEE'S NEXT FENCING LESSON.
PAY ATTENTION, SIRE! I'M ABOUT TO SHOW YOU SOMETHING RATHER UNUSUAL!
HE'S NOT KIDDING EITHER! HEH! HEH!
MACHINE

HOWL!
IT WORKED!

THAT WAS SMASHING, TEACHER! WILL YOU SHOW ME HOW TO DO IT, PLEASE?
DAZE
SO!

AND WHEN YOU'VE FINISHED THAT SPOT OF FENCING, I'LL SHOW YOU ANOTHER USE FOR A SWORD!
HUH! I CAN GUESS WHAT THAT IS!

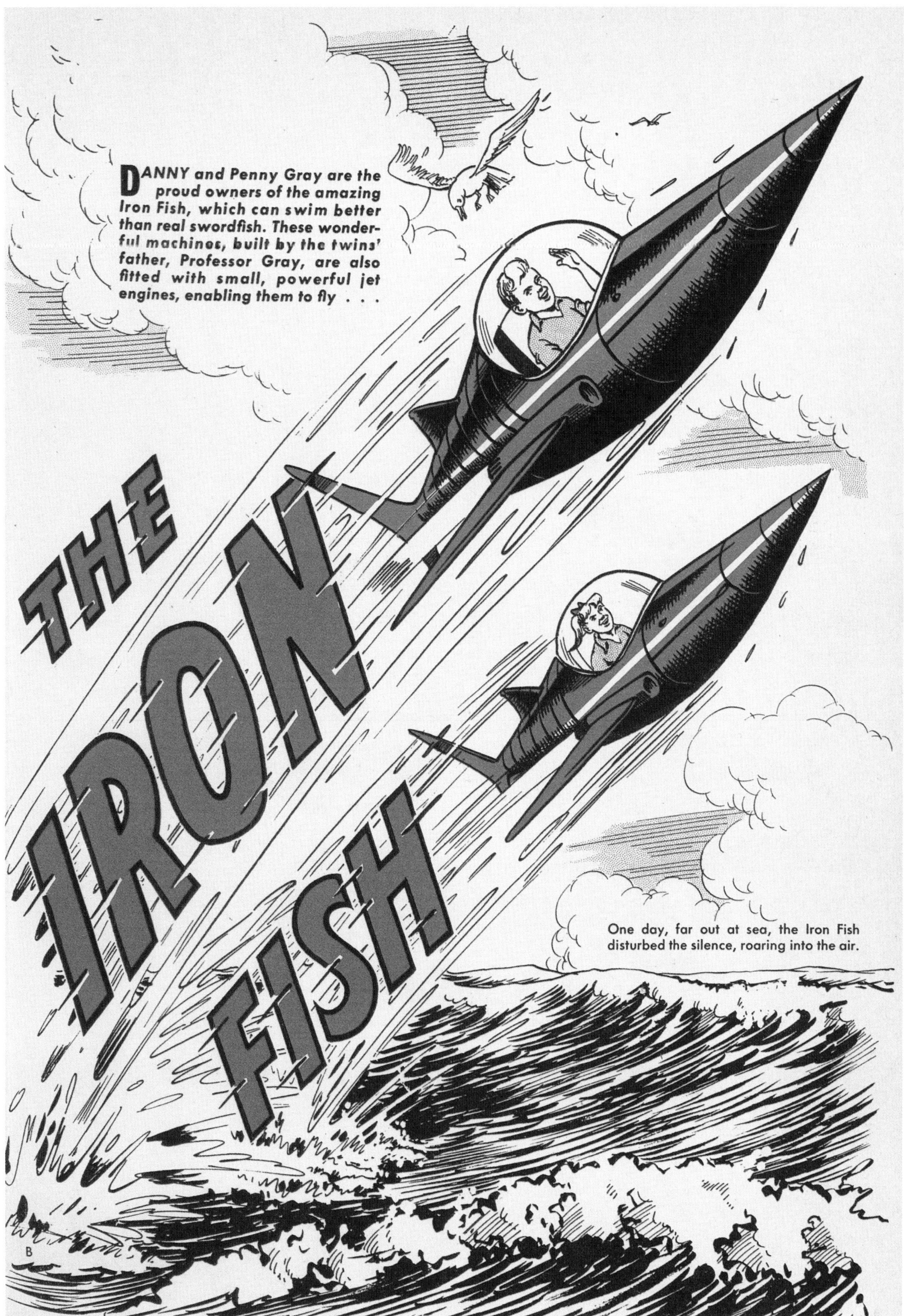
DANNY and Penny Gray are the proud owners of the amazing Iron Fish, which can swim better than real swordfish. These wonderful machines, built by the twins' father, Professor Gray, are also fitted with small, powerful jet engines, enabling them to fly . . .
THE IRON FISH
One day, far out at sea, the Iron Fish disturbed the silence, roaring into the air.
B

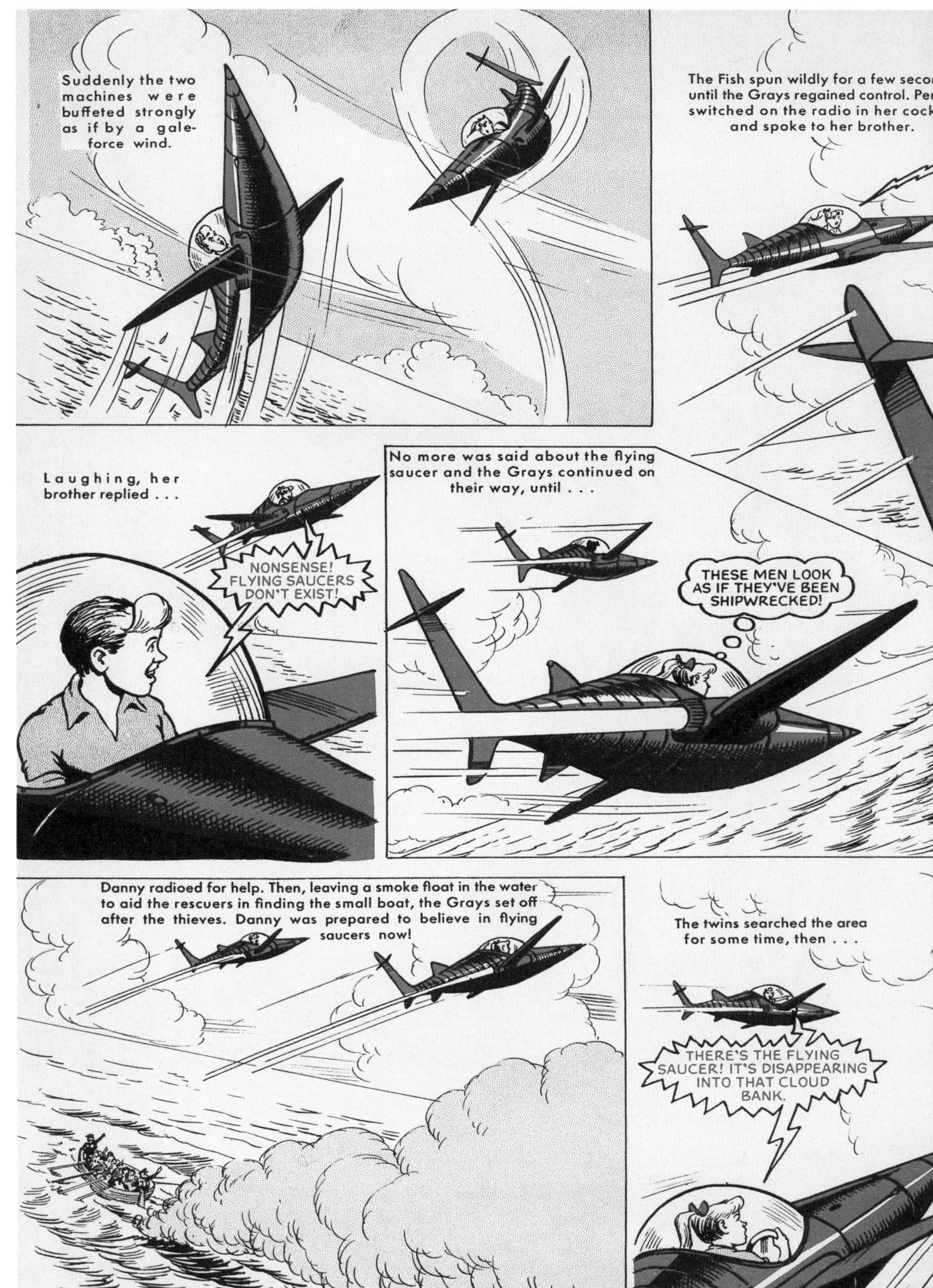
Suddenly the two machines were buffeted strongly as if by a gale-force wind.
The Fish spun wildly for a few secon
until the Grays regained control. Pen
switched on the radio in her cock
and spoke to her brother.
Laughing, her brother replied . . .
NONSENSE! FLYING SAUCERS DON'T EXIST!
No more was said about the flying saucer and the Grays continued on their way, until . . .
THESE MEN LOOK AS IF THEY'VE BEEN SHIPWRECKED!
Danny radioed for help. Then, leaving a smoke float in the water to aid the rescuers in finding the small boat, the Grays set off after the thieves. Danny was prepared to believe in flying saucers now!
The twins searched the area for some time, then . . .
THERE'S THE FLYING SAUCER! IT'S DISAPPEARING INTO THAT CLOUD BANK.

M SURE I SAW SOMETHING LIKE A FLYING SAUCER FLASH OVERHEAD JUST BEFORE WE WERE BLOWN ABOUT!
e Grays landed side the boat. The n told a strange story . . .
OUR SHIP WAS ATTACKED BY STRANGE MEN IN A FLYING SAUCER! THEY STOLE OUR CARGO, THEN SET US ADRIFT AND SUNK THE SHIP.
They followed the strange craft.

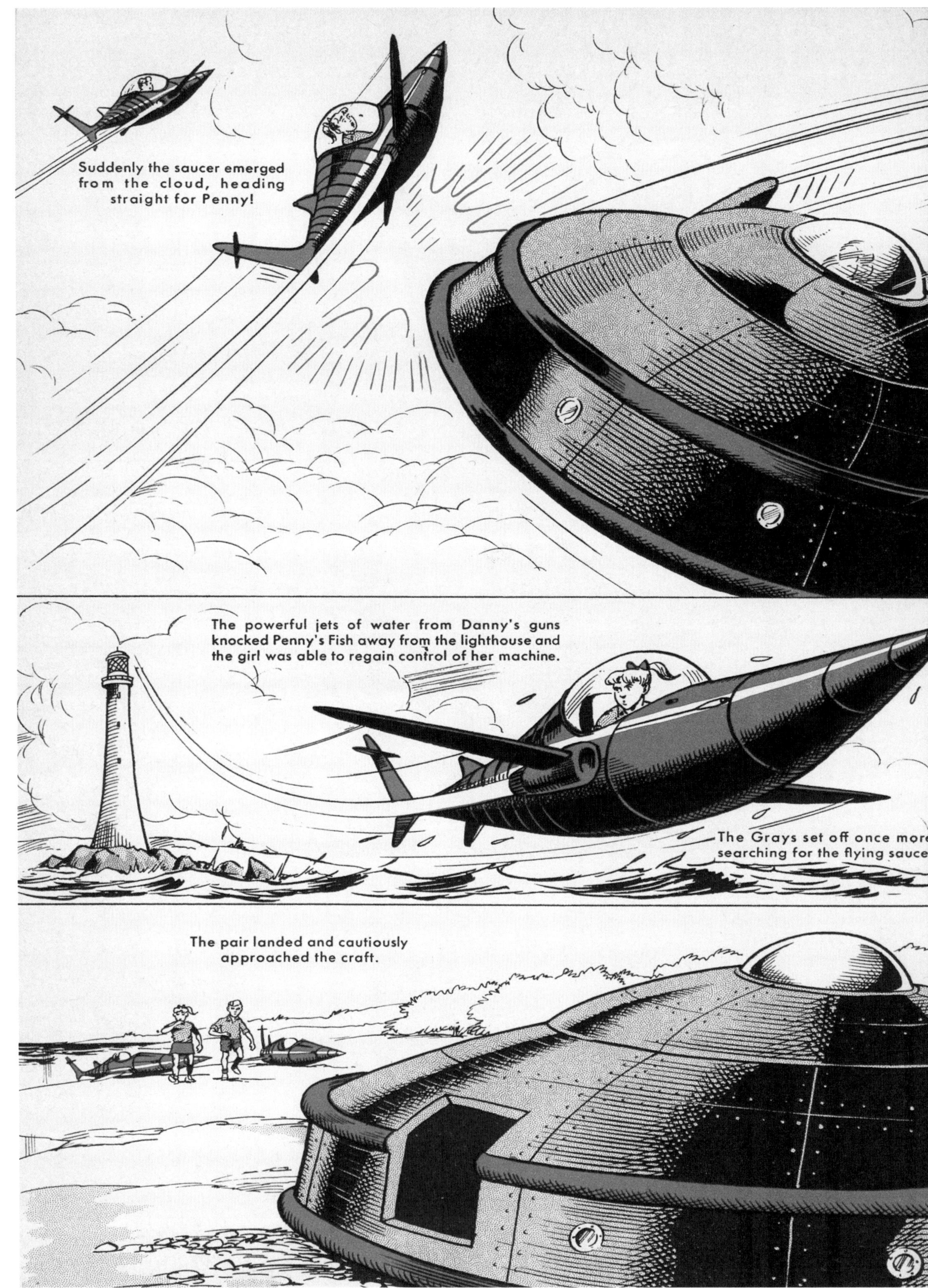
Suddenly the saucer emerged from the cloud, heading straight for Penny!
The powerful jets of water from Danny's guns knocked Penny's Fish away from the lighthouse and the girl was able to regain control of her machine.
The Grays set off once more searching for the flying saucer
The pair landed and cautiously approached the craft.

Out of control, Penny's Fish spiralled downwards.
CRUMBS! I'M GOING TO HIT THAT LIGHTHOUSE!
Danny dived to his sister's aid. He pressed a button in the cockpit . . .
And, before long, they found it. It had landed on the beach of a lonely island.
Danny and Penny were bundled into the saucer.

The weird man locked the Grays in a small cabin. Then the saucer took off.
WE'RE HEADING OUT TO SEA.
The Grays landed in the sea. They were miles from the coast. How could they get back to dry land?
The Grays swam the few yards to the Fish. Once again they were ready to track down the saucer and its strange occupants.
Some time later, on the lonely
the saucer had visited earlie

Suddenly, far out at sea . . .
The whole floor of the cabin had swung downwards. As the twins fell, the saucer headed back towards land.
I HOPE YOUR PLAN WORKED, PENNY.
IT DID. LOOK— THERE ARE THE IRON FISH WAITING FOR US!
All the time Penny was in the saucer, she had been making the Iron Fish follow them. The girl had done this by means of a small remote control gadget no bigger than a transistor radio.
Suddenly . . .

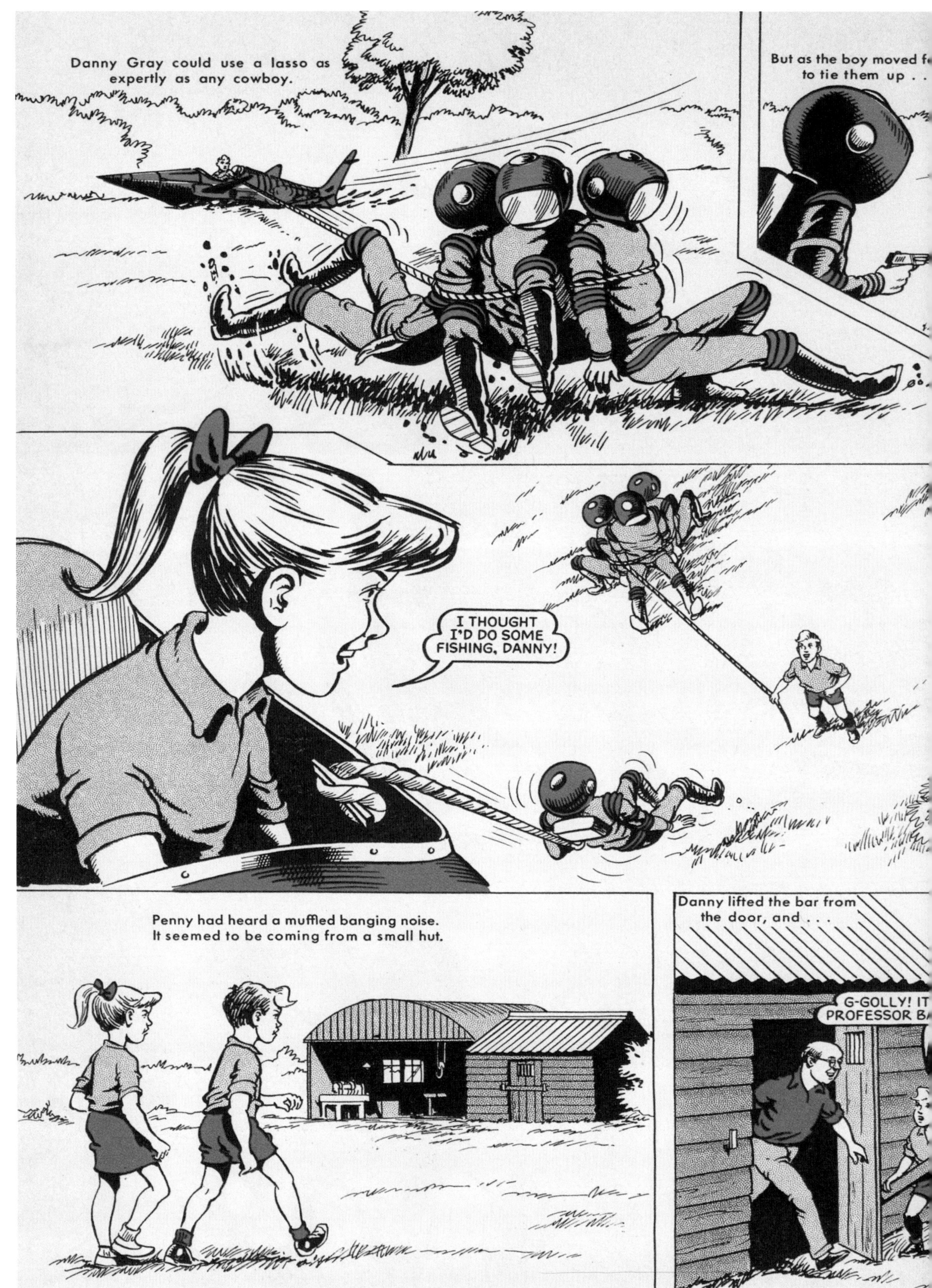
Danny Gray could use a lasso as expertly as any cowboy.
But as the boy moved
to tie them up . . .
I THOUGHT I'D DO SOME FISHING, DANNY!
Penny had heard a muffled banging noise. It seemed to be coming from a small hut.
Danny lifted the bar from the door, and . . .
G-GOLLY! IT
PROFESSOR

Then . . .
RIGHT! LET'S GET THE POLICE TO DEAL WITH THESE CHARACTERS. WHOEVER THEY ARE.
JUST A MINUTE. I THOUGHT I HEARD SOMETHING.
Soon . . .
Professor Barr was an old friend of Professor Gray.
THEY TOOK ME PRISONER ALL RIGHT, BUT...

...THEY'RE NOT FROM OUTER SPACE—THEY'RE AS HUMAN AS YOU OR I! THEY STOLE THE FLYING SAUCER I INVENTED, AND THESE HIGH-SPEED PRESSURE SUITS. THEY INTENDED USING THE SAUCER TO BRING OFF LARGE SCALE ROBBERIES!
The Professor told the twins he'd built his laboratory on the island to keep his latest invention secret. But the crooks had got wind of it.
Soon the thieves were behind bars. And Danny and Penny had found a friend to join their games in the sky.
THE END

DENNIS the MENACE
ONE MINUTE TO NINE.....
PUFF! GASP! I'LL HAVE TO THINK OF SOME WAY OF GETTING TO SCHOOL EARLIER— WITHOUT LOSING MY SLEEP!
SO—
BANG!
THUMP!
DENNIS'S HUT
BANG!
BANG!
NEXT MORNING...
Z-Z-Z!
THE ALARM CLOCK RINGS AT FIVE TO NINE AS USUAL...
CHOP!
BRR-R-R!
1 CWT.
THE WEIGHT CATAPULTS DENNIS OUT OF BED......
...INTO A TUB OF ICY WATER, WHICH WAKENS HIM UP...
AND MAKES HIM JUMP OUT INTO HIS JERSEY HANGING READY NEARBY.
ON WITH MY TROUSERS AND INTO MY SHOES....
HUP!
PRETTY SMART, EH?
YOU'RE IMPROVING! IT'S ONLY TWO MINUTES TO NINE.
ONLY GOT T'RUN AT HALF SPEED NOW!

THE
BASH STREET
BEARS
BASH ST. ROCK

FAR OUT IN THE WEST IS THIS ONE-HORSE TOWN...

AS YOU PASS ALONG THE MAIN STREET, YOU MAY SEE THE HORSE
STORE

ENTER TEACHER—
CRUNCH!
CRUNCH!

STOP THAT NOISE!

GULP!
GULP!

GOOD TO SEE THEM ALL SO BUSY!

HM! NICE SMELL!

WHAT'S THIS?—TOFFEE!

THEN—
CRUNCH!
CRUNCH!
SCHOOL
MORE NOISE!

CRUNCH!
CRUNCH!
CRUNCH!
THE EXPLOSION STUCK THE TOFFEE TO THE WALLS!

SEPTEMBER

TURN LEFT FOR BASH STREET...
BASH ST.

THEN YOU COME TO THE SCHOOL...
SCHOOL
CRUNCH!
CRUNCH!
IS THIS THE SOUND OF TINY MARCHING FEET?

NO—IT'S THE SOUND OF GREAT GNASHING TEETH! THE TEETH BELONG TO THE BASH STREET SCHOOL PUPILS...
CRUNCH!
CRUNCH!

AY, WE HAVE A CHEMISTRY ESSON FOR THE BOYS...
BOO!

...AND A COOKERY LESSON FOR THE GIRL.
FOOD! HOORAY!

SOON—

ONE LITTLE BEAR IS MAKING BUBBLE GUM—

THE BUBBLE GROWS AND GROWS...

BLUP!

H!
H!
COTT
WOOL

HEY! IT'S SNOWING!

HO! HO! THEY THINK IT'S TIME TO START HIBERNATING FOR THE WINTER!
YAWN!
YAWN!

BUT—
ZZZZZZ!
THEY'RE STILL NOISY!

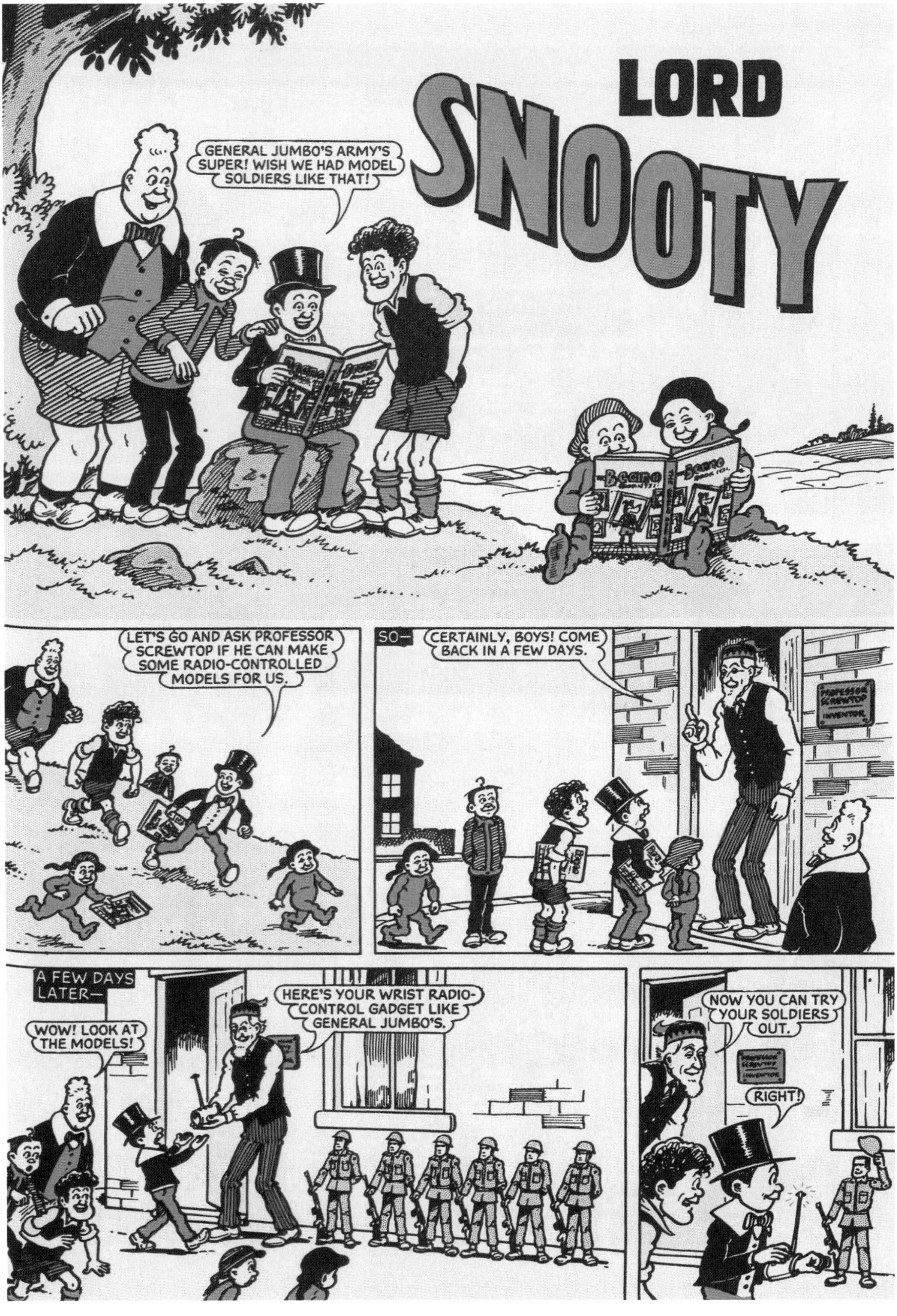

LORD SNOOTY

GENERAL JUMBO'S ARMY'S SUPER! WISH WE HAD MODEL SOLDIERS LIKE THAT!

Models muddle into puddle!

The pals beat a hasty retreat!

What a mishap! Snooty's army's scrap!

DENNIS THE MENACE
AND GNASHER
WHAT ARE THAT LOT UP TO TODAY?
I DO LOVE STICKING ON THESE LOVELY FLOWERS.
OUR FLOAT WILL SOON BE READY FOR THE PARADE.
THEY'RE IN THE CARNIVAL PARADE. WE MUSTN'T MISS THIS!

The float they're making will soon have folk quaking!
WE'LL ENTER TOO!
NO FLOWERS FOR US— JUST THISTLES!
THE MENACES
BANG!
NAILS
WHAT DO YOU THINK OF OUR ENTRY, READERS?

RIGHT! HERE WE ARE!
THE MENACES
START OF PARADE
HUH! YOU HAVEN'T ANYTHING TO THROW TO THE CROWD!
NICE, SOFT FLOWERS!
OH, YES WE HAVE!
FLOUR
FLOUR
STINK BOMBS
FLOUR
WATER

A nasty surprise from three bad guys!
NASTY NIFF
PONG
HOW AWFUL!
THE CROWD DON'T LIKE IT—BUT I DO!
SPLOOSH!
RAT-TAT-TAT!
FLOUR
FLOUR
FLOUR
FLOUR

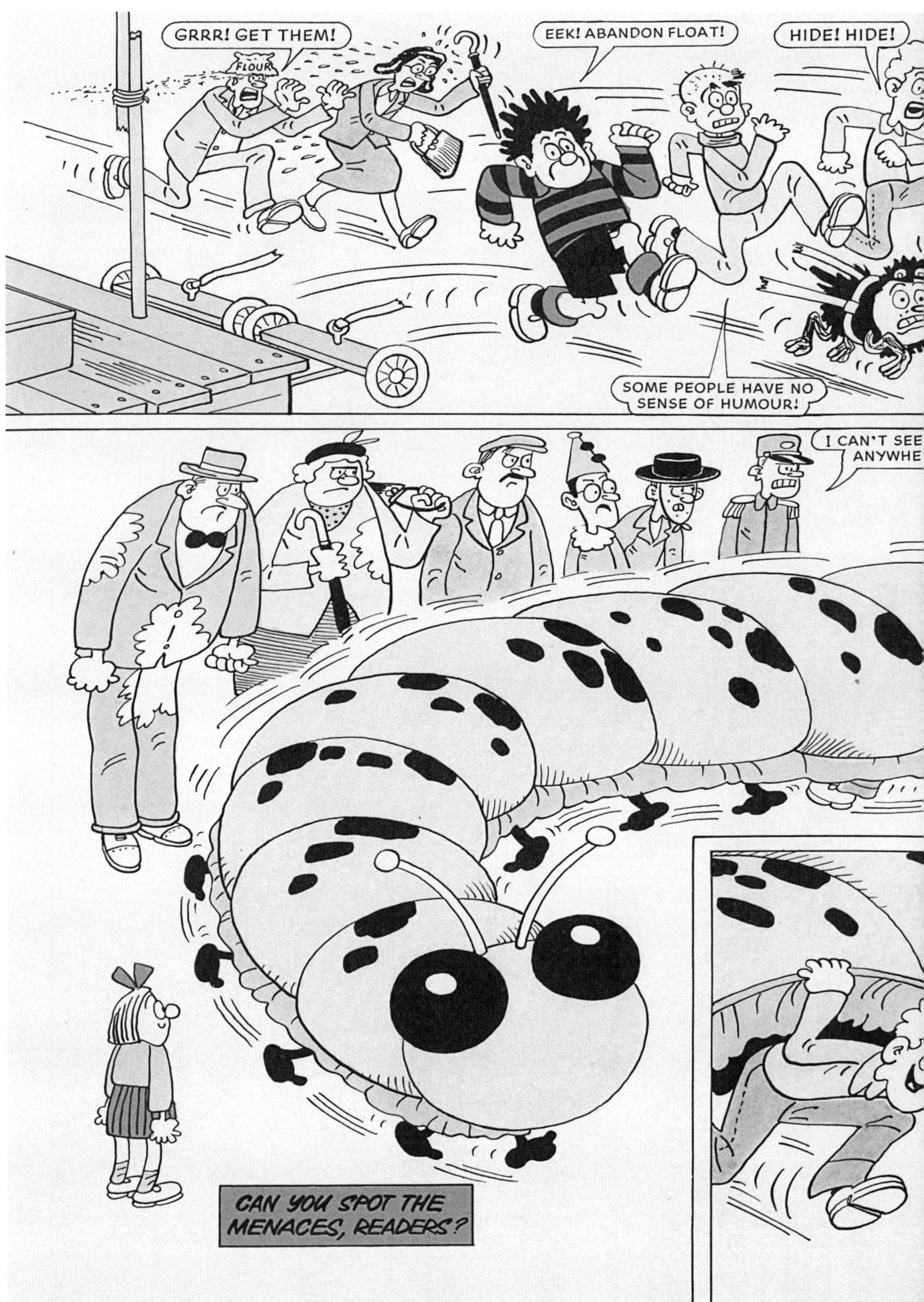
GRRR! GET THEM!
FLOUR
EEK! ABANDON FLOAT!
HIDE! HIDE!
SOME PEOPLE HAVE NO SENSE OF HUMOUR!
I CAN'T SEE
ANYWHE
CAN YOU SPOT THE MENACES, READERS?

H!WE'VE LOST THEM!
FLOUR
E WE ARE, READERS! HO! HO!

THE MENACES
THAT PARADE TURNED OUT TO BE GREAT FUN!
YEAH! I WISH IT WASN'T OVER!
IT'S NOT!
WE'VE DECIDED TO HAVE ANOTHER CARNIVAL OF OUR OWN!
EEK! OUR DADS!

THE STRONG MAN'S DAUGHTER

CAN I HELP YOU?
SHRIEK! AN EARTHLING!
INTER-GALACTIC ATLAS

ER . . . WE'VE BROKEN DOWN — WE WERE ON OUR WAY TO MARS.
I'LL GET YOU HOME . . .

. . . GET INTO YOUR SHIP!

MARS IS THAT BIG RED PLANET, ISN'T IT?
ER . . . YES!

So—
THROW!
SAFE JOURNEY!
MARS
THE MILKY WAY
INTERGALACTIC DAIRIES

Meanwhile—
BETTER NOT MENTION THIS — NO-ONE'LL EVER BELIEVE ME!
PANSY POTTER

BETTER NOT MENTION THIS — NO-ONE'LL EVER BELIEVE US!
WELCOME TO MARS
NO LITTER PLEASE!

46
BIFFO
the BEAR

ALL THIS WEEK THE AMAZING
BIFFO
ON WITH THE SHOW!
THE AMAZING BIFFO

Soon, on stage—
UP! UP!
FLOAT

MAGIC!
FANTASTIC!
CLAP!
CLAP!

WEE THE AMAZING
BIFFO
Later—
EEK!

Har! Har! A trick car?

ROGER the DODGER
I WONDER IF THE NEWS IS ON.
GREETINGS, EARTHLINGS! LAST NIGHT YOUR WORLD WAS TAKEN OVER BY THE ALL POWERFUL PLANET OF ZUKONIA. WE ARE IN TOTAL CONTROL OF EARTH AND YOU MUST OBEY ALL OUR ORDERS!
HERE ARE THE ZUKONIAN RULES...
Disguising his voice
...WITH IMMEDIATE EFFECT, SPROUTS AND CABBAGE ARE ILLEGAL. ANYONE CAUGHT COOKING THEM WILL BE VAPOURISED!
OH, MY GOODNESS!
DON'T WANT TO BE CAUGHT BY THE ZUKONIANS!
ZOOM!

RULE TWO - WE WANT EARTHLINGS TO BE HAPPY. ONLY CARTOONS TO BE SHOWN ON YOUR TELEVISUAL BOXES!
QUICK! CHANGE THIS!
CLICK!
BUT I WAS WATCHING A FASCINATING PARTY POLITICAL BROADCAST!
ALL SCHOOLS HAVE BEEN CLOSED! EXCEPTIONAL CHILDREN WILL BE TAUGHT TO SPEAK ZUKONIAN, WHICH WILL BE TRANSMITTED TO THEM THROUGH THOUGHT WAVES.
WATCH THIS! IT'LL BE A GREAT LAUGH!

SPURGLE! WARGLE! BLOOP!
MY SON – AN EXCEPTIONAL CHILD! WHAT DOES 'SPURGLE WARGLE BLOOP' MEAN, ROGER?

SPURGLE MEANS 'YOU'VE'...
YES!
WARGLE MEANS 'BEEN'...
YES, YES!

MUNCH!
...AND BLOOP MEANS 'DODGED!' BYEEE!
GROAN! AND I HAVE BEEN WELL AND TRULY!
VROOM!

CALAMITY JAMES
THE WORLD'S UNLUCKIEST YOUTH
WHEEZE! SWEAT! FLAP!
DAANG!
TRASH T.V.
BEEP! BEEP!
ALEXANDER LEMMING - JAMES'S FAITHFUL BUT RATHER CHEEKY PET.
HO-HO! JAMES'S LUCK IS WORSE THAN EVER! CHORTLE!
OOF! OUCH! OOYAH!
TOTTER
GOLD
WINNING LOTTERY TICKET.
DOH-H! I CAN'T TAKE MUCH MORE OF THIS!
MAYBE YOUR OLD PAL, PROFESSOR BONKERS, CAN HELP, JAMES.
GOOD IDEA, THAT LEMMING! LET'S SEE IF HE'S IN!
PROFESSOR BONKERS
FRIENDLY NEIGHBOURHOOD MAD SCIENTIST.
PRESS!
BIFF!
GNNNNOOOMPH!
SPROINGG!
AH! JAMES! I SEE YOU'VE DISCOVERED MY AUTOMATIC DOUBLE GLAZING SALESMEN DISCOURAGER!
BLITHER! YES - WORKS WELL! TWITTER!
STAGGER!

YOU MUST HELP ME, PROF! I NEED SOMETHING TO STOP ME GETTING HURT ALL THE TIME!
TINKLE! PLINK!
AHA! I HAVE THE VERY INVENTION...
...MY BOUNCY, RUBBER-BALL SUIT. IT SHOULD GIVE YOU ALL THE PROTECTION YOU NEED.
BUS STOP
BOYOINGG!
COOL!
SEE! EVERYTHING JUST BOUNCES OFF IT!
BRILLIANT, PROF!
DOINGG!
BOUNCE!
Nearby–
THE GAMES OVER, M'MAN! OUR BALL'S LIKE BURST!
PHSSSS!
HEAVY, MAN!
GAME ON, MAN! JAMES MAKES A GROOVY BASKETBALL!
WAAAAAAAAH!
OVER HERE, DUDE!
BOING! BOING! BEDOING!

LOB!
GREAT SHOT, MAN!
AAAARGH! HE-E-E-ELP!
BLADOING!
BYOINK!
THWAAP!
So–
WE'LL TRY THIS UNBREAKABLE PLASTIC DOME NEXT!
ER...OK!
THERE! SAFE AND SOUND!
YOU'RE A GENIUS, PROF!
KLUNK!
THUD!
TODDLE!
PING!
UH-OH! I FORGOT ABOUT MANHOLES!
BLAAT!
NYAAAAAAA!
PLUMMET!
Next...
NEVER MIND! MY REMOTE-CONTROLLED ROBOT BODYGUARD WILL SEE THAT YOU COME TO NO HARM!
WOW!

WAHOO! ALL THIS STUFF THAT SHOULD BE HITTING ME IS HITTING THE ROBOT INSTEAD.
THAANG!
PYOINK!
DONGG!
KLANK!
WHAT'S THIS BIG RED BUTTON FOR, PROFESSOR?
N-NO! DON'T PRESS THAT, WHAT EVER YOU DO!
CLICK!
A-TTACK! BEEP! A-TTACK!
THAT'S THE ATTACK BUTTON! RUN FOR IT!
FLEE!
BEEP! A-TTACK! A-TTACK! BEEP!
BASH!
BOOT!
Many hours of painful pounding later...
ER- THE BATTERIES HAVE RUN OUT AT LAST! HOW LUCKY'S THAT?
WHIRR! PHUT!
GIBBER! BLITHER! BLEHHHH!
SEMI-CONSCIOUS SLAVER!
TEE-HEE! NOW THE PROFESSOR NEEDS PROTECTION FROM JAMES! SNIGGER!
GRRRAAAAGH!
NOW, NOW! TEMPER-TEMPER!

BALL BOY
WE'VE GOT AN AWAY GAME TODAY.
HOPE THAT THIS MIST DOESN'T PUT THE GAME OFF.
IT'S NOT MIST - OLD BETSY'S ENGINE HAS GONE UP IN SMOKE.
SORRY! BUS BROKEN!
LOOKS LIKE WE'LL NEED SOME OTHER FORM OF TRANSPORT.
I KNOW...
DAVE EASTBURY

...WE CAN POGO TO THE MATCH.
GREAT IDEA, EH?
But–
BOING!
THUD!
CRUNCH!
D-DUH! GUESS WHO FORGOT ABOUT THIS TUNNEL?
Back home–
THIS OLD OUTBOARD MOTOR FROM DAD'S SPEEDBOAT WILL DO THE TRICK!

HOLD TIGHT!
WOWP! NOT TIGHT ENOUGH!
ZOOM!
CRUMP!
THAT WAS SORE, THAT WAS!
Later–
THIS OLD SUPPORTERS FLAG AND THE CORNER FLAGS MAKE A GREAT HANG-GLIDER.
WE'LL GET THERE IF IT KILLS US!
THAT'S QUITE POSSIBLE!

WE HAVE LIFT OFF!
WHEEE! UP, UP AND AWAY!

WE'RE NEARLY THERE!

But–
...AND THE WIND WILL SWITCH DIRECTION AND INCREASE TO GALE FORCE...

WHOOSH!
...TOLD YOU!
H–E–L–P–!

Much later–
WE'VE COME RATHER A LONG WAY!

KAPLOP!
WHAT A DISASTER!
NOT REALLY...
...WE'RE HAVING AN AWAY GAME AFTER ALL!

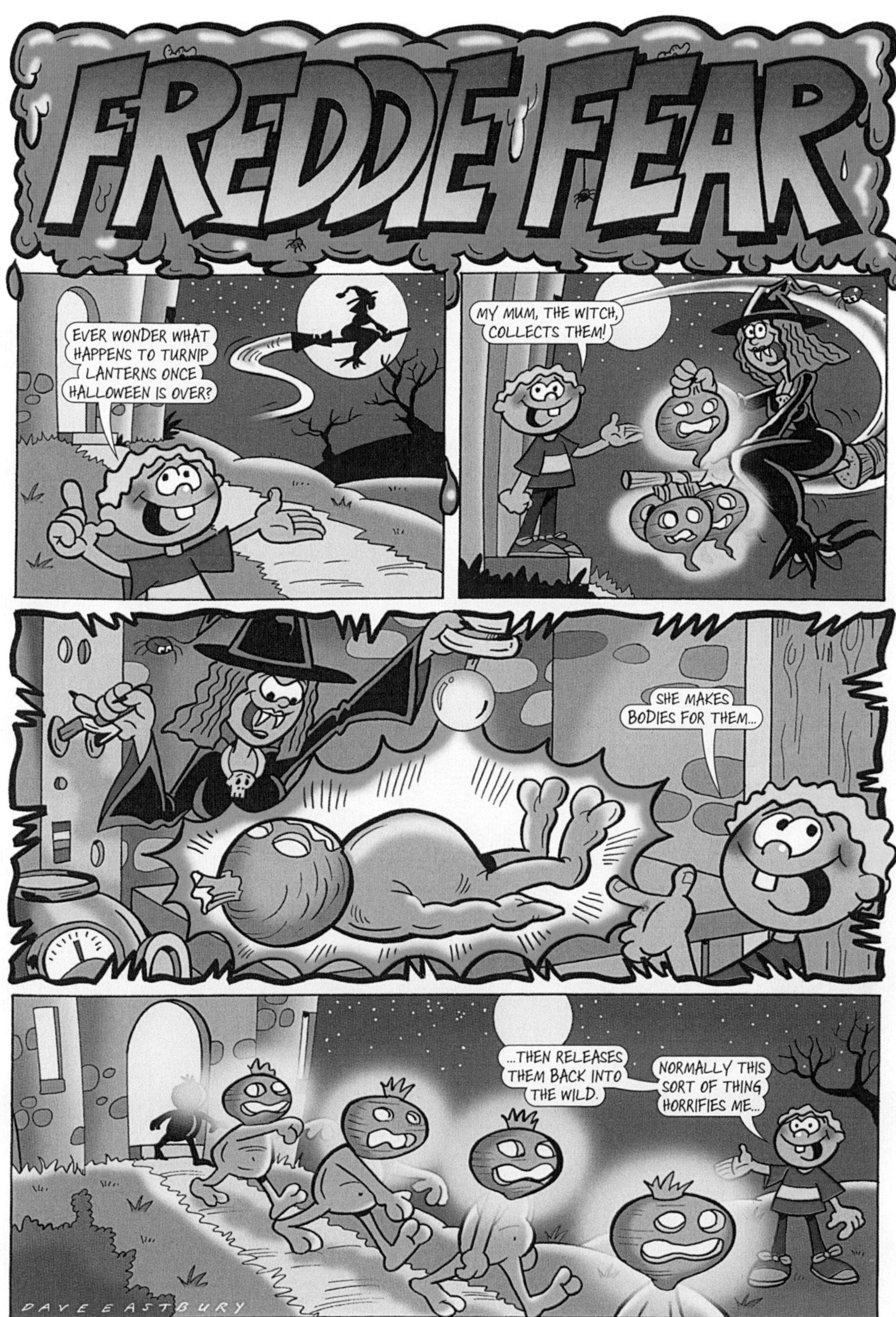
FREDDIE FEAR
EVER WONDER WHAT HAPPENS TO TURNIP LANTERNS ONCE HALLOWEEN IS OVER?
MY MUM, THE WITCH, COLLECTS THEM!
SHE MAKES BODIES FOR THEM...
...THEN RELEASES THEM BACK INTO THE WILD.
NORMALLY THIS SORT OF THING HORRIFIES ME...
DAVE EASTBURY

...BUT NOT WHEN THEY MAKE GREAT TEAM-MATES FOR NIGHT MATCHES AGAINST BALL BOY'S TEAM!

Everybody was quite shocked when Desperate Dan started his wire-pulling. But Dan wasn't at all burnt-up when he was used as an electric plant.

MINNIE
ROTTEN OL' DAD'S CONFISCATED MY GOOD WEAPONS JUST 'COS I USED HIS PRIZE MARROW AS A TORPEDO. LOOK AT THE BROKEN CATTYS AN' THINGS THAT ARE LEFT!
KNOCK KNOCK
SOMEBODY'S KNOCKIN' ON THE DOOR, MINNIE!
BUSTED
BENT
LEAKY
MINNIE
WHO'S KNOCKIN'? -OOH! IT'S A BATTERING RAM!
TAP TAP
THE NEIGHBOURHOOD KIDS ARE SICK OF YOU ALWAYS BULLYING 'EM, SO THEY'VE MADE ME THEIR LEADER. I'M GOING TO BASH YOU!
BITE
OH, YEAH? YOU AND WHOSE ARMY, FATTY FUDGE?
WAIT TILL WE GET OVER MINNIE'S HUT – THEN WE PULL THE PLUG OUT!
INK
ITCHING POWDER
CRASH
THIS ARMY!
CAMOUFLAGE
CRASH!
RICE PUD
CAMOUFLAGED PERISCOPE
CAMOUFLAGE NET
DUCK POND
GLUE
OH, BOTHER! IT'S TWELVE O'CLOCK – WE'LL HAVE TO GO FOR DINNER – NEVER MIND, WE'LL COME BACK AFTER AND FINISH MINNIE OFF.
BOING BOING BOING
WE CAN'T STAY HERE – FATTY'S ARMY 'LL FLATTEN US WHEN THEY GET BACK! WE'LL HAVE TO FIND A NEW HEADQUARTERS.
MINNIE'S GANG HUT

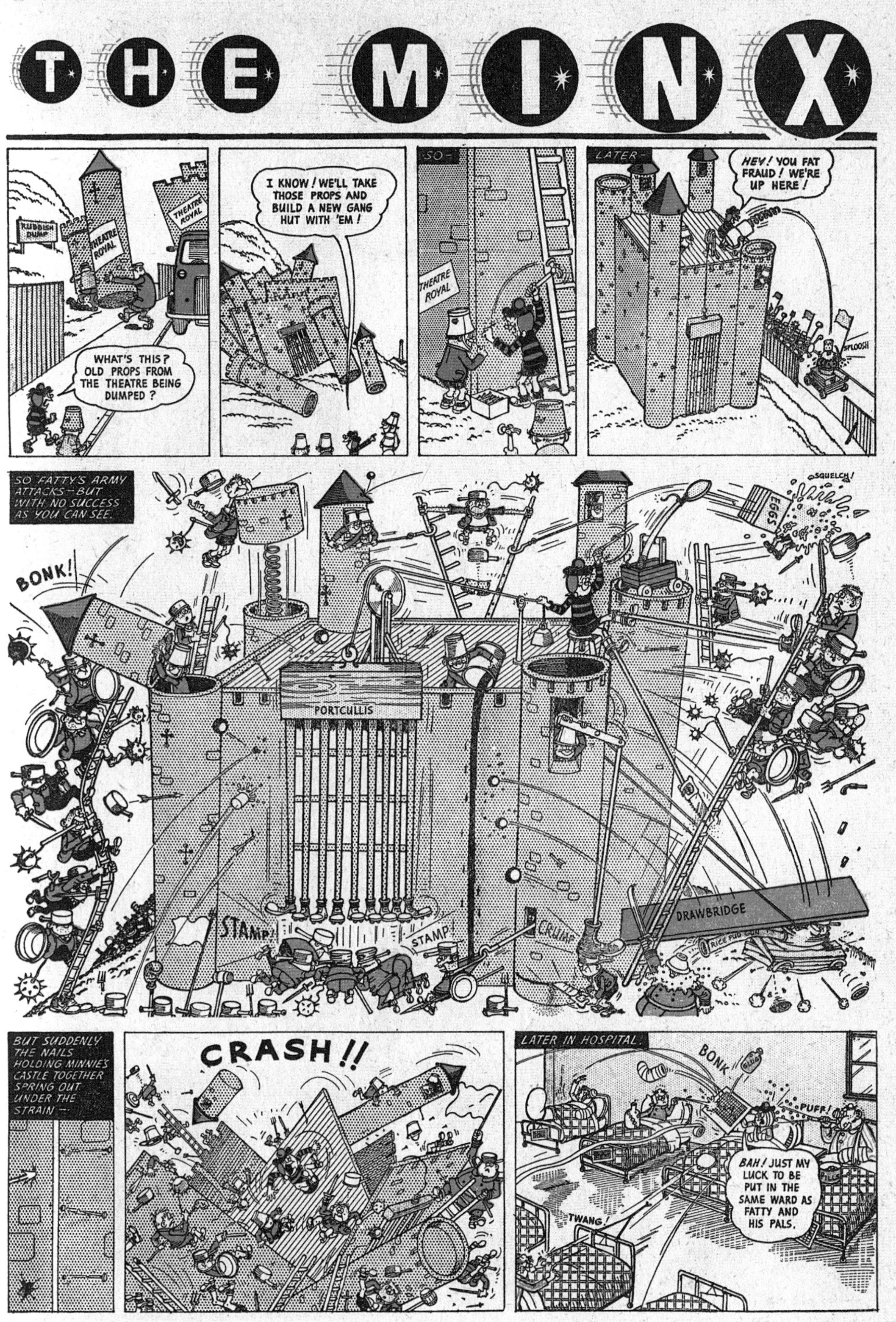
THE MINX
RUBBISH DUMP
THEATRE ROYAL
THEATRE ROYAL
WHAT'S THIS? OLD PROPS FROM THE THEATRE BEING DUMPED?
I KNOW! WE'LL TAKE THOSE PROPS AND BUILD A NEW GANG HUT WITH 'EM!
SO-
THEATRE ROYAL
LATER-
HEY! YOU FAT FRAUD! WE'RE UP HERE!
SPLOOSH
SO FATTY'S ARMY ATTACKS—BUT WITH NO SUCCESS AS YOU CAN SEE.
SQUELCH!
EGGS
BONK!
PORTCULLIS
STAMP!
STAMP!
CRUNF
DRAWBRIDGE
RICE PUD GUN
BUT SUDDENLY THE NAILS HOLDING MINNIE'S CASTLE TOGETHER SPRING OUT UNDER THE STRAIN—
CRASH!!
LATER IN HOSPITAL.
BONK
PUFF!
BAH! JUST MY LUCK TO BE PUT IN THE SAME WARD AS FATTY AND HIS PALS.
TWANG!

LORD SNOOTY AND HIS PALS
I'VE INVENTED A CYCLE-COPTER. WOULD YOU LIKE TO SEE IF IT FLIES? I'M GETTING TOO OLD TO CYCLE NOW.
NO, THANKS, PROFESSOR SCREWTOP.
ALL RIGHT, I'LL DO IT MYSELF. YOU UNGRATEFUL KIDS~AFTER ALL THE THINGS I'VE INVENTED FOR YOU!
IT FLIES ALL RIGHT!
OOH! MY RHEUMATICS!
CRASH
MY GREENHOUSE!
5 MINUTES LATER
YOU'VE MADE A HOLE RIGHT THROUGH LORD SNOOTY'S GREENHOUSE.
TO PAY FOR THE DAMAGE YOU CAN HAVE THE NEW CORN CURE I'VE INVENTED. YOU'LL FIND IT IN MY LABORATORY.
IN THE LAB
AH! HERE IT IS. WE'LL SET UP A CORN-CURING BUSINESS AND EARN SOME MONEY.
CORN CURE
ROLL UP, FOLKS, AND TRY LORD SNOOTY'S CORN CURE~ WE SPRAY IT ON.
HUH! NOBODY SEEMS TO WALK ROUND HERE.
CORN CURE
HA! HA! I'M SITTING!
I'M CYCLING!
CHIROPODIST CORNS CUT AND CURED.
IN
OUT
CORNS
AND THE FOLK WHO DO WALK GET SPLENDID SERVICE AT THE CORN-CURING SHOP.
CINEMA
SEE HOW PEOPLE DROP THEIR CINEMA TICKETS WHEN THEY COME OUT OF THE PICTURE HOUSE.
YES, THAT GIVES ME AN IDEA. COLLECT THEM ALL.
LATER
FREE CINEMA TICKETS at the TOP OF STRAGGLY HILL
FREE CINEMA TICKETS! AH!~ I'M OFF TO GET SOME!
UP THE HILL~ QUICKLY!

FREE CINEMA TICKETS (USED ONES)
IT'S A TWIST!
WE'VE HAD A WEARY WALK FOR NOTHING!
HA! HA! NOW IT'S SNOOTY'S CHANCE TO USE HIS CORN CURE!

COME THIS WAY, GENTLEMEN, IF YOUR FEET ARE SORE. WE'LL FIX YOUR CORNS WITH OUR SOOTHING CORN CURE!
OH! MY POOR FEET!
THAT'S RIGHT. GET YOUR SOCKS OFF!
GOSH! IT FEELS QUEER.
CORN CURE

OUCH! IT'S BURNING MY FEET. MY CORNS ARE WORSE THAN EVER!
HOWL

YOU LITTLE TWISTERS! NOW WE'VE GOT CORNS AND BLISTERS!
CYCLES FOR HIRE
RUN, GANG! LUCKY FOR US THEY CAN'T RUN FAST WITH THEIR SORE FEET.

CYCLES FOR HIRE
HELP! THEY'VE ALL HIRED BIKES.
GOT YOU!

2 MINUTES LATER
I'M FED UP WITH THIS CORN CURE. SPRAY IT OVER THE FENCE.
GET RID OF THE STUFF!
Z-Z-Z

HOORAY
HULLO! THAT SOUNDS LIKE FARMER JONES!

I'LL BUY THAT STUFF FROM YOU, SNOOTY. COME OVER AND SEE WHAT IT'S DONE TO THE WEEDS IN MY CORNFIELD.
£5 FIVE POONS!

IT'S A CORN CURE SURE ENOUGH, BUT NOT FOR FEET. IT KILLS WEEDS!

AT THE HOSPITAL
OH, PROFESSOR! LORD SNOOTY'S CHUMS ARE EATING ALL YOUR FRUIT AND CHOCOLATE.
YES, THEY BROUGHT IT FOR ME, BUT I'M SO BANDAGED UP THEY'RE HAVING TO EAT IT THEMSELVES!
YES, WE'RE VERY SORRY TO HAVE TO DO THIS!
D. WATKINS

THE DANGER MAN
THE Danger Man from Mars, and Jane and Jet, his young assistants known as the Danger Minors, have pledged themselves to tackle any task for the benefit of mankind, no matter how dangerous. They travel the globe in fast, Martian-built rocket ships, the Zoomar and the smaller Zoomets.
D
D
DM
DM

One day, as the Zoomar and Zoomets flashed through the sky over a vast, Australian desert, the Danger Man's attention was attracted by a cluster of buildings below. This was the famous rocket-launching site of Woolloowonga.
Their air-cushion brakes hissing, the three machines dropped swiftly to earth and landed neatly beside a huge rocket which was in position ready to be fired. The controller of the site, Professor Howell, eagerly greeted the three famous visitors.
LET'S TAKE A CLOSER LOOK AT THAT ROCKET-LAUNCHING SITE, KIDS.
He told them that the rocket about to be launched was to carry a capsule containing two monkeys into orbit round the Earth and then bring them back to safety again.
Tears welled up in Jane's eyes when she saw the monkeys being secured into the capsule by the scientists. "The poor little things," she sobbed. "It seems so cruel to shut them up in there!"
The Danger Man placed a comforting arm round Jane's shoulders, and a thoughtful look came over his face.
Suddenly, he marched with Jane up to Professor Howell, and made an offer that was to thrill the whole world....

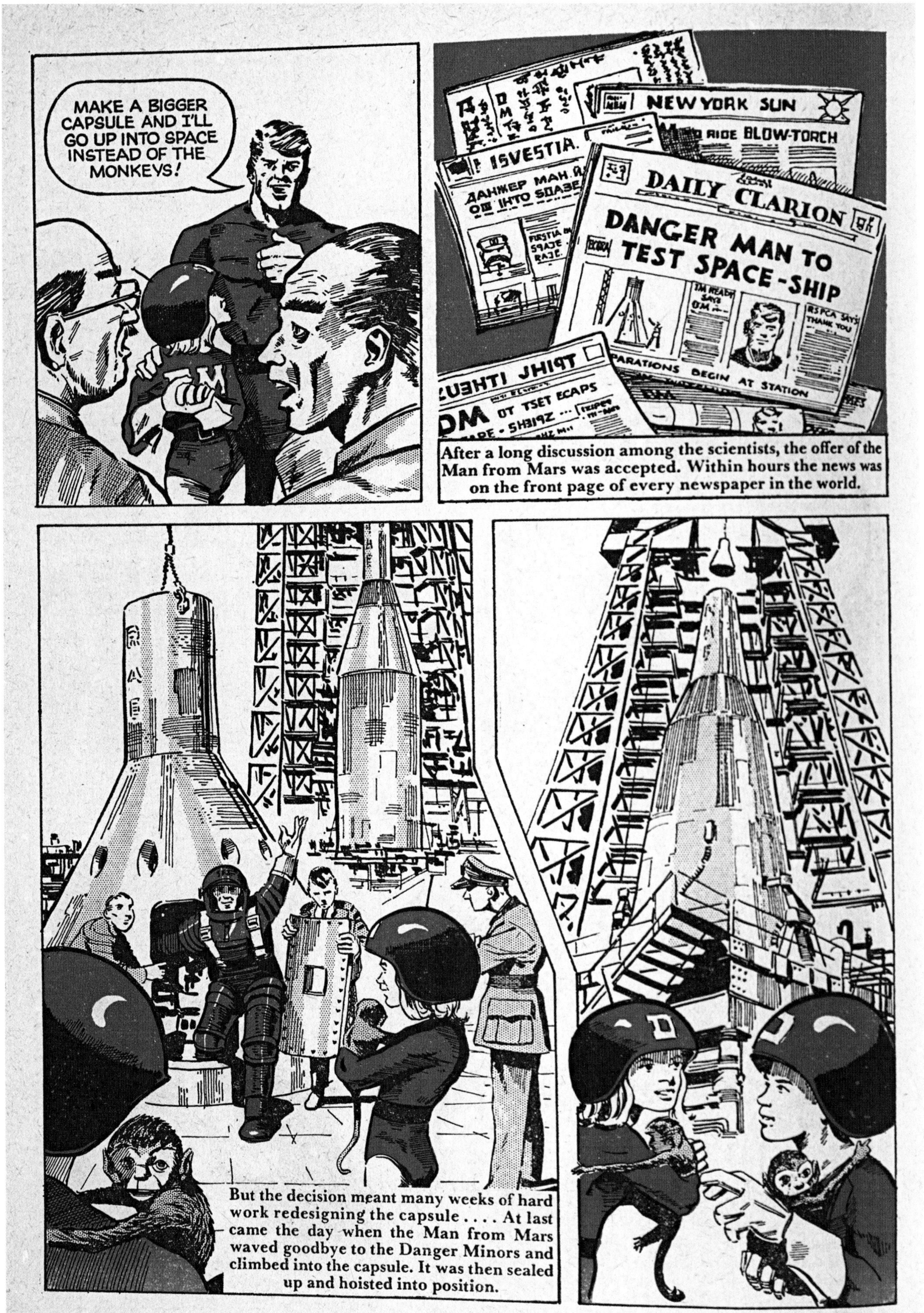

After a long discussion among the scientists, the offer of the Man from Mars was accepted. Within hours the news was on the front page of every newspaper in the world.

But the decision meant many weeks of hard work redesigning the capsule .... At last came the day when the Man from Mars waved goodbye to the Danger Minors and climbed into the capsule. It was then sealed up and hoisted into position.

All was ready for the launching, and Jane and Jet accompanied Professor Howell to the rocket control room. Then, at Zero Hour, the rocket roared skywards, carrying the Danger Man's capsule into the unknown.

One by one, the various stages of the rocket were shed as the capsule was thrust towards space, and at last the final stage of the rocket fell away. The conical capsule containing the Man from Mars then began to circle the Earth like a tiny moon. Everything was going to plan.

Inside the capsule, the Danger Man carefully checked the many dials on the instrument panel before sending an "All's well" message back to Earth by way of his special wireless.

But no sooner had he done so, when disaster struck! By a million to one chance a meteor hurtlin
through space struck the capsule a glancing blow! The instruments were shattered and the Danger Ma
knocked unconscious by the violent jerk....
In the control room at Woolloowonga, the radar operator, who had been following the capsule'
course on his screen, suddenly gasped as the image of the space capsule wavered across the screen. Then hi
face paled. "There's been an accident!" he gasped. "The capsule's out of our control. We can't bring it bac
to Earth!" The Danger Minors looked grimly at each other Then Jet's mouth tightened. "Come on, Jane
We've got to rescue the Danger Man!" he snapped.

GMT
HOLD

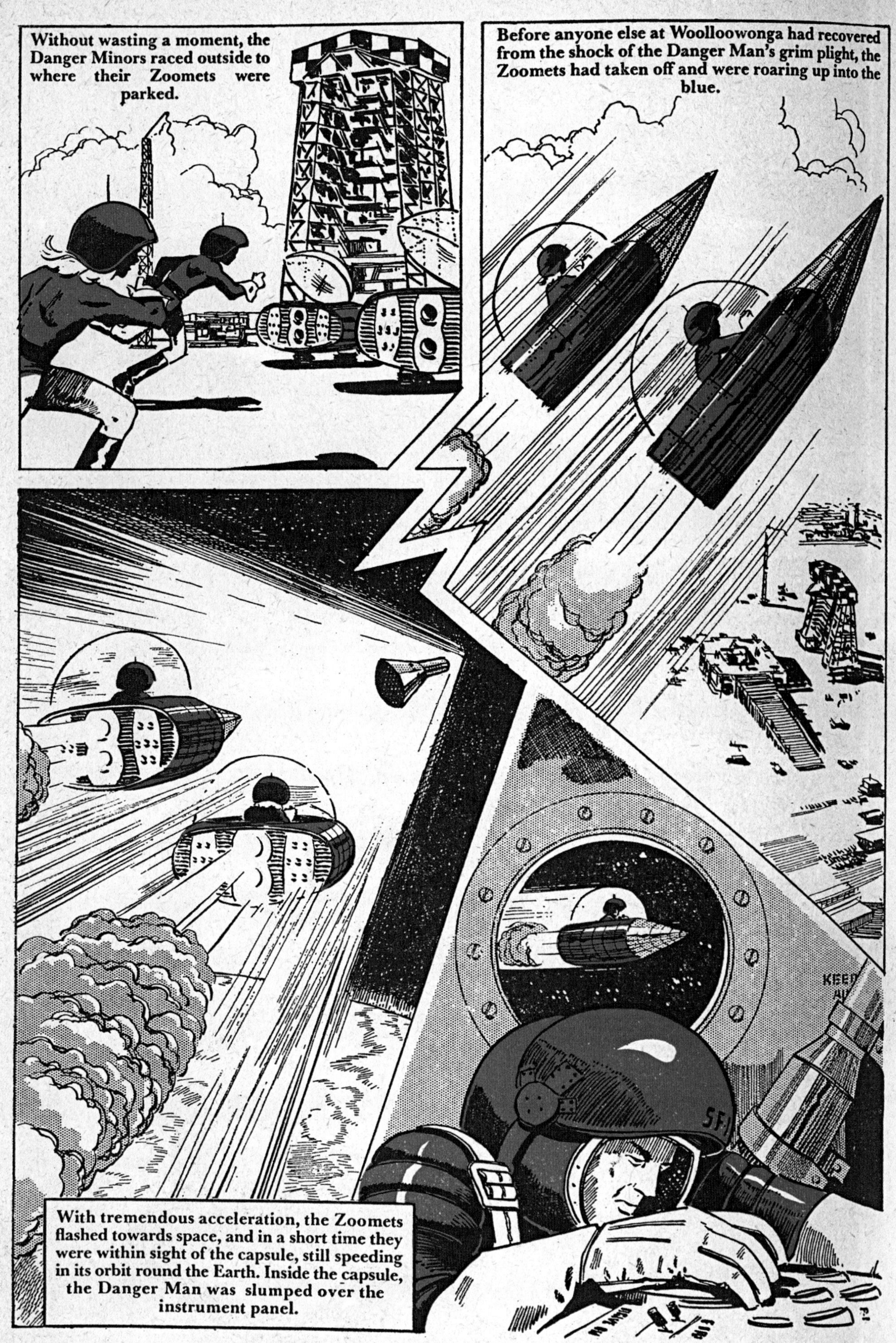
Without wasting a moment, the Danger Minors raced outside to where their Zoomets were parked.
Before anyone else at Woolloowonga had recovered from the shock of the Danger Man's grim plight, the Zoomets had taken off and were roaring up into the blue.
With tremendous acceleration, the Zoomets flashed towards space, and in a short time they were within sight of the capsule, still speeding in its orbit round the Earth. Inside the capsule, the Danger Man was slumped over the instrument panel.

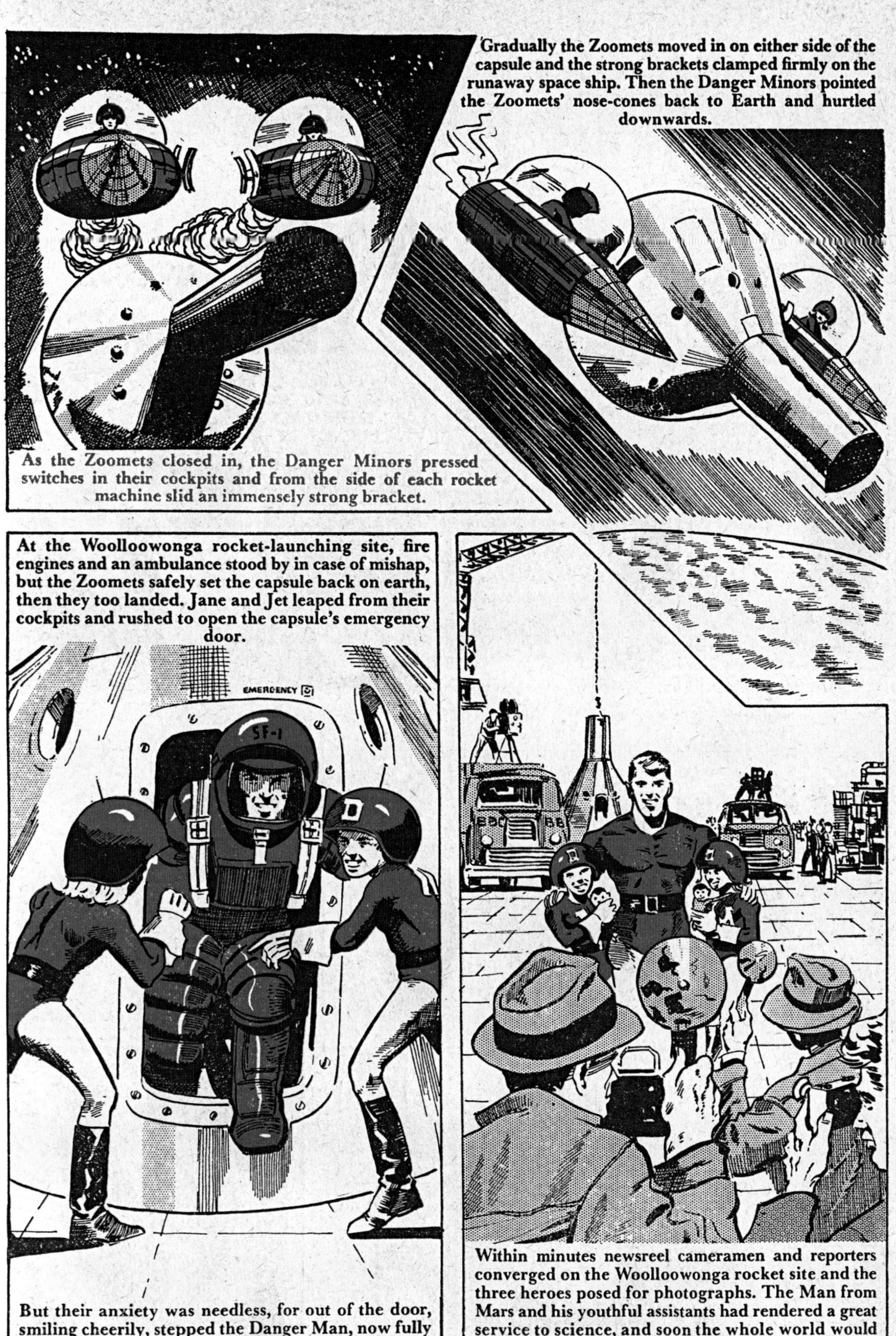
As the Zoomets closed in, the Danger Minors pressed switches in their cockpits and from the side of each rocket machine slid an immensely strong bracket.
Gradually the Zoomets moved in on either side of the capsule and the strong brackets clamped firmly on the runaway space ship. Then the Danger Minors pointed the Zoomets' nose-cones back to Earth and hurtled downwards.
At the Woolloowonga rocket-launching site, fire engines and an ambulance stood by in case of mishap, but the Zoomets safely set the capsule back on earth, then they too landed. Jane and Jet leaped from their cockpits and rushed to open the capsule's emergency door.
EMERGENCY
SF-1
D
But their anxiety was needless, for out of the door, smiling cheerily, stepped the Danger Man, now fully recovered and none the worse for his experience.
Within minutes newsreel cameramen and reporters converged on the Woolloowonga rocket site and the three heroes posed for photographs. The Man from Mars and his youthful assistants had rendered a great service to science, and soon the whole world would know about it.

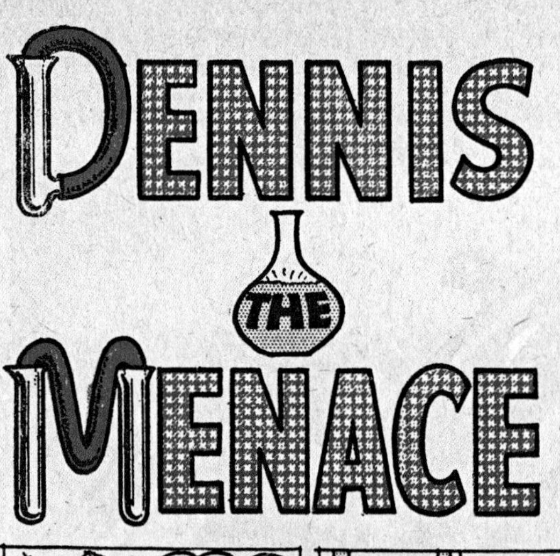
DENNIS
THE
MENACE

DENNIS I WANT YOU TO—

—CHOP UP SOME FIREWOOD!
WOOSH!

HUH! CHOP UP SOME FIREWOOD, INDEED! A BUSY CHAP LIKE ME!

LOOK AT THAT NOW!—JUST THE THING FOR MAKIN' STINK BOMBS!
Chemistry Set
TOY SHO

H'M! IF I WAS TO MARCH UP TO DAD AND DEMAND A CHEMISTRY SET, HE'D SAY—
NO!

AND IF I WAS TO ASK HIM NICELY, HE'D SAY—
NO!

SO I'LL JUST DEMAND ONE! I'VE NOTHING TO LOSE!

DAD! I MUST HAVE A CHEMISTRY SET RIGHT NOW!
YES, CERTAINLY, MY BOY!

OKAY, OKAY! I ONLY ASKED!

GOOD GRIEF. HE SAID 'YES!'

WOOSH!
TOY S
Chemistry Set
YOU'D BETTER DO YOUR EXPERIMENTS IN YOUR OLD HUT, DENNIS.
OKAY, POP!
DENNIS
Chemistry Set
LATER
FIZZ!
HISS!
GURGLE!
GURGLE!
PLOP!
DENNIS
BANG
TUM-TI-TUM!
SORRY ABOUT THE H-HUT, DAD! SOMETHING WENT WRONG.
NOTHING WENT WRONG, MY BOY! I KNEW THIS WOULD HAPPEN IF I GAVE YOU A CHEMISTRY SET. THANKS FOR THE FIREWOOD!

Rusty's a dandy fixer-upper—His radio can cook his supper!

RUSTY

LOOK WHAT I'VE BOUGHT, MUM! A RADIO AS USED IN THE NAVY. IT'S SWELL, ISN'T IT?
HMM. TAKE IT AWAY UPSTAIRS OUT OF MY WAY, RUSTY.

LATER
A FEW LITTLE REPAIRS AND IT'LL BE IN FIRST CLASS WORKING ORDER.

OH, RUSTY! THE ELECTRIC IRON'S BUST. CAN YOU HELP ME TO FIX IT?

JUST YOU GIVE IT TO ME, MUM. I'LL FIX IT FOR YOU!

HMM! MAYBE I SHOULD HAVE FINISHED ONE JOB BEFORE I STARTED THE OTHER. NOW I'VE GOT ALL THE BITS MIXED UP!

AH! THIS IS THE BIT I WAS LOOKING FOR, TO PUT IN MY RADIO! I'LL FINISH THE RADIO FIRST.

THAT'S THE RADIO FIXED! I'LL PLUG IT IN AND LET IT WARM UP, WHILE I MEND MUM'S IRON DOWN STAIRS.

AN HOUR LATER
THERE YOU ARE, MUM. THE IRON'S FIXED, AND IT WOULD HAVE COST YOU PLENTY AT THE ELECTRICIAN'S.
THANKS, RUSTY!

HMM! THAT'S FUNNY! IT DOESN'T SEEM TO BE HEATING UP!

WOW! MY RADIO!
GOODNESS! A HOLE IN THE CEILING. HOW DID THAT HAPPEN?

IT'S YOUR FAULT, RUSTY. YOU'VE SHOVED THE WORKS FROM THE IRON INTO YOUR RADIO AND IT'S BURNED THROUGH THE FLOOR OF YOUR BEDROOM!

FUNNY! THIS IRON WORKS LIKE A RADIO NOW. IT'S NOT VERY LOUD BUT IT'S BETTER THAN NOTHING!

THE BASH STREET KIDS
THE BASH STREET KIDS ARE GOING INTO ACTION WITH ALL THE DEADLIEST DEVICES THAT THEIR CRAFTY LITTLE MINDS CAN THINK UP... AND NO WONDER! BEHIND THAT WALL IS A TEACHERS' CONVENTION... DOZENS OF TEACHERS SIMPLY ASKING TO BE MOBBED!
BASH STREET AIR FORCE INTERCONTINENTAL MISSILE
PARASOLE TROOPER
TEACHER TWEEZERS
SUCK!
SUCK!
SUCK!
SUCK!
BASH STREET AIR FORCE (PART 2)
BOMBS (ROTTEN EGGS)
BASH STREET TEACHERS' CONVENTION
BASH STREET KIDS DO NOT ENTER.
TEACHER ANTI-TANK GUN
T.N.T.
WOOOOOOOOM!
BASH ST. BEATNIK
BEAT-PIK
WOODPECKER WITH ARMOUR-PLATED BEAK.
BONK! BONK!
CRUMP!
NOW TURN THE PAGE FOR A BIG SURPRISE!

BUT THE REASON FOR THE TEACHERS' CONVENTION WAS TO DISCUSS COUNTER-MOVES AGAINST THE KIDS! SO....
ZOOM
SPLOP!
SPLOP! SPLOP! SPLOP! SPLOP! SPLOP! SPLOP!
SUCK!
GLUE
Z-O-O-M
PYOING!
CRUNCH!
SUCK!
YOU WERE WARNED!
CROW WITH ARMOUR-PLATED BEAK
SPLOP!
SQUOOOOSH!
BONK!
GLUE
BONK! BONK! BONK!
SPLAT!
Z-I-P-P-P!
CLANG!
MAGNET
ITCHING POWDER

Desperate Dan's gum bubble turns the town into rubble!

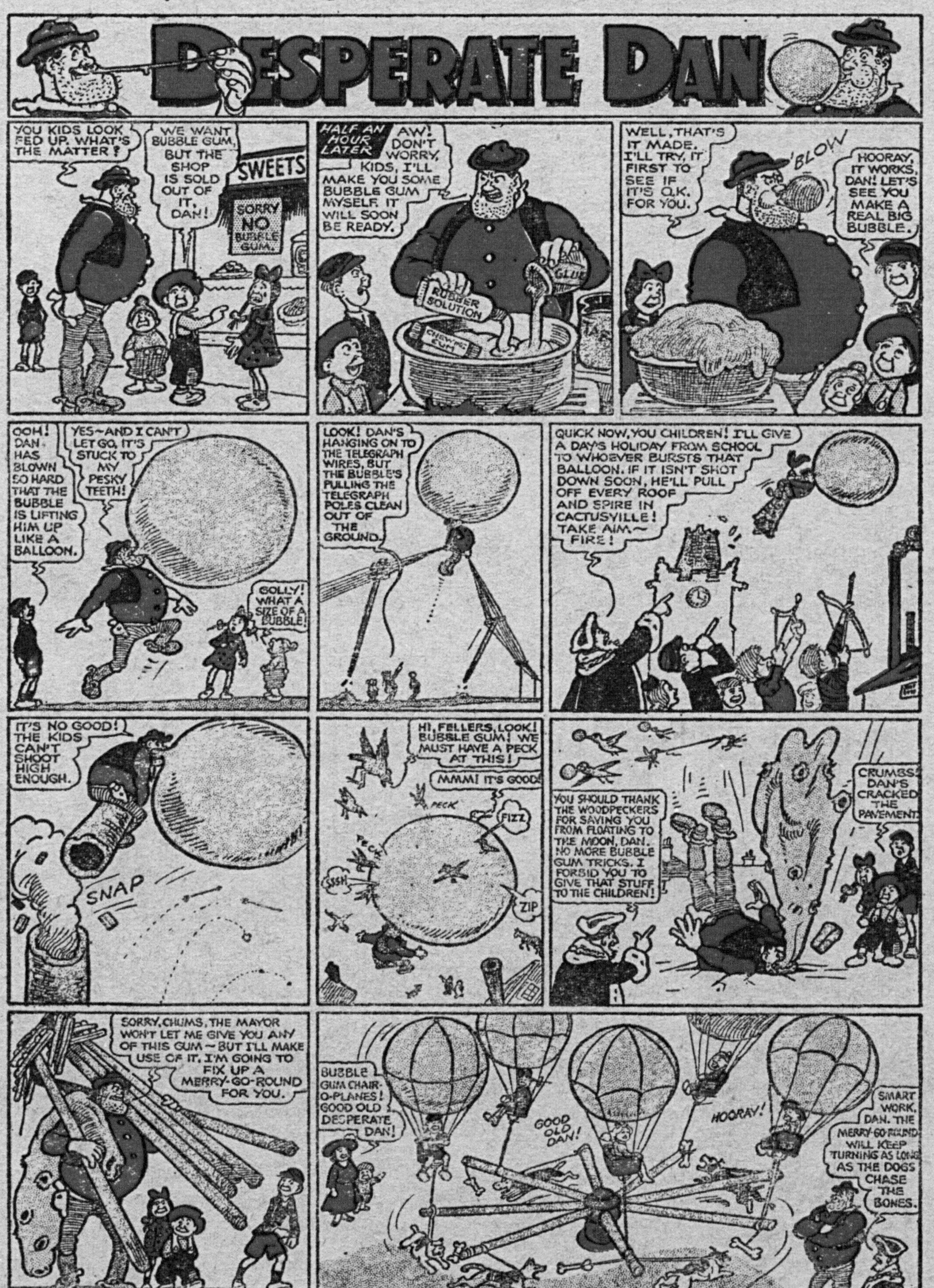

LORD SNOOTY
IF YOU WASH ALL THE DISHES AND POLISH THE FLOOR IN TEN MINUTES I'LL GIVE YOU THIS BIG BASKET OF FRUIT!
DEAR! DEAR! POOR SNITCHY AND SNATCHY HAVE GOT FLATTENED IN THE RUSH!
SPLASH WASH WIPE
Z-Z-Z
NINE MINUTES LATER
THE DISHES ARE NEARLY ALL DRIED NOW. I HOPE YOU TWO WILL HAVE THE FLOOR POLISHED WITHIN THE TEN MINUTES!
GASP
SWEAT
THE TEN MINUTES ARE UP—AND THE FLOOR'S POLISHED. PHEW!
HA! HA! IT'S SO SLIPPERY THAT SNOOTY'S SLIPPED ON IT AND SMASHED SIX EGG CUPS!
OH! MY GOODNESS!
CRASH
YOU CARELESS BOY! UNTIL YOU BUY ME SIX MORE EGG CUPS THERE'LL BE NO FRUIT FOR ANY OF YOU!
WE'LL SEND SNITCH AND SNATCH OUT FOR CUPS RIGHT AWAY!
IN A CHINA SHOP
WE'LL HAVE HALF A DOZEN OF THOSE EGG CUPS, PLEASE!
EGG CUPS
TEE-HEE! HE'LL HAVE TO BORROW A LADDER TO CLIMB UP TO THEM. HA! HA!
THAT'S WHAT YOU THINK!
SUCK
PHEW!
GREAT SCOTT!
WITH THESE RUBBER SUCTION PLATES ON YOUR FEET YOU CAN WALK UP WALLS LIKE A FLY!
GOODY! GOODY! WE'LL BUY TWO SETS OF THESE! WE COULD USE 'EM!
IT'S A BIT OF A JOB WALKING HOME WITH 'EM ON YOUR FEET! THEY SUCK THE ROAD AT EVERY STEP!
EGG CUPS
PLOP!
SEE THAT? AUNT MAT'S PUTTING THE FRUIT ON A HIGH SHELF SO THAT THE GANG CAN'T HAVE ANY UNTIL WE DELIVER THE EGG CUPS!
EGG CUPS
GOOD STUFF! THAT SUITS US FINE!
KITCHEN WINDOW
IN THE KITCHEN
YOU SEE, AS LONG AS WE HANG ON TO THE EGG CUPS, SNOOTY AND THE GANG WON'T GET ANY FRUIT AT ALL!
EGG CUPS

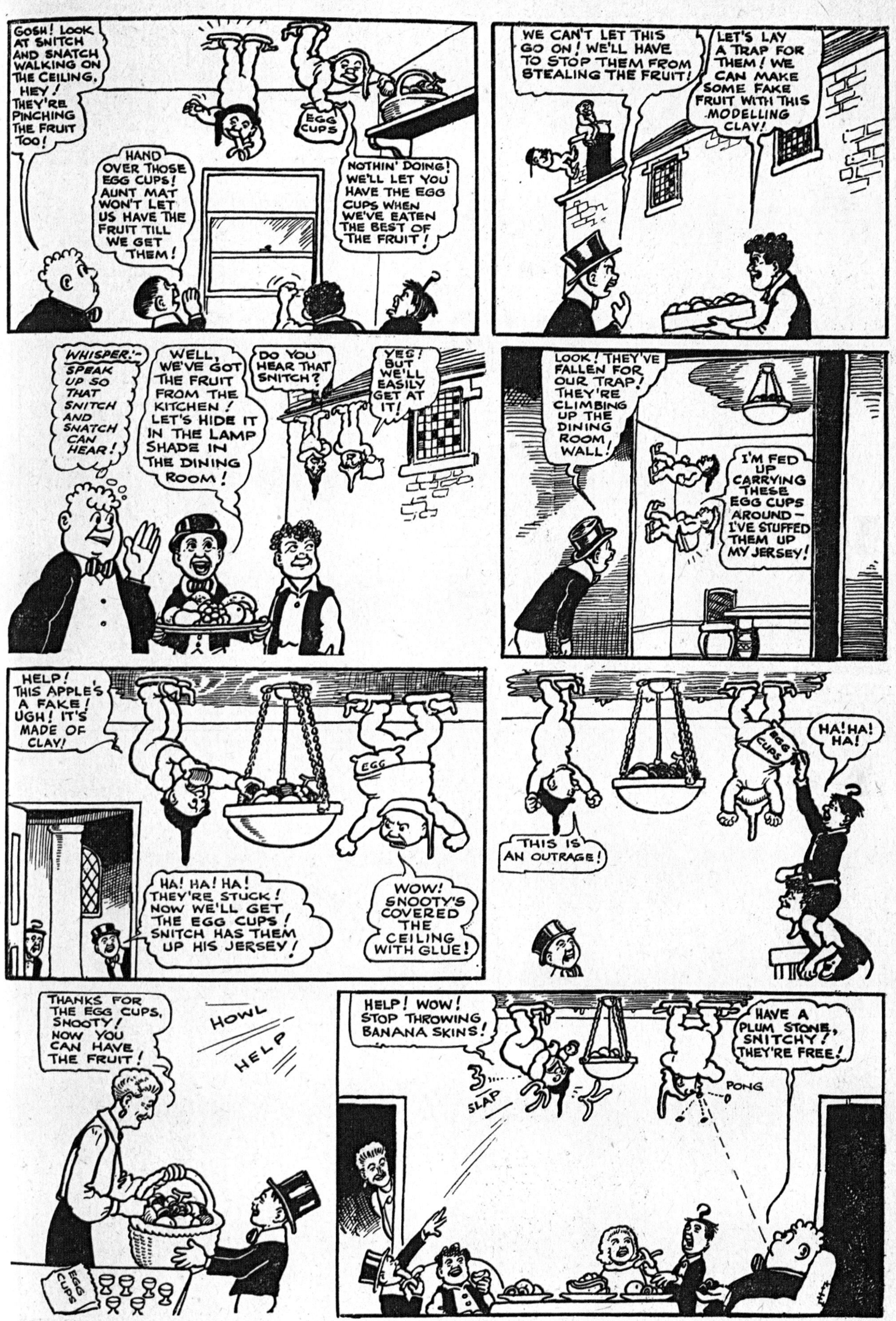
GOSH! LOOK AT SNITCH AND SNATCH WALKING ON THE CEILING. HEY! THEY'RE PINCHING THE FRUIT TOO!
EGG CUPS
HAND OVER THOSE EGG CUPS! AUNT MAT WON'T LET US HAVE THE FRUIT TILL WE GET THEM!
NOTHIN' DOING! WE'LL LET YOU HAVE THE EGG CUPS WHEN WE'VE EATEN THE BEST OF THE FRUIT!
WE CAN'T LET THIS GO ON! WE'LL HAVE TO STOP THEM FROM STEALING THE FRUIT!
LET'S LAY A TRAP FOR THEM! WE CAN MAKE SOME FAKE FRUIT WITH THIS MODELLING CLAY!
WHISPER:- SPEAK UP SO THAT SNITCH AND SNATCH CAN HEAR!
WELL, WE'VE GOT THE FRUIT FROM THE KITCHEN! LET'S HIDE IT IN THE LAMP SHADE IN THE DINING ROOM!
DO YOU HEAR THAT SNITCH?
YES! BUT WE'LL EASILY GET AT IT!
LOOK! THEY'VE FALLEN FOR OUR TRAP! THEY'RE CLIMBING UP THE DINING ROOM WALL!
I'M FED UP CARRYING THESE EGG CUPS AROUND - I'VE STUFFED THEM UP MY JERSEY!
HELP! THIS APPLE'S A FAKE! UGH! IT'S MADE OF CLAY!
EGG
HA! HA! HA! THEY'RE STUCK! NOW WE'LL GET THE EGG CUPS! SNITCH HAS THEM UP HIS JERSEY!
WOW! SNOOTY'S COVERED THE CEILING WITH GLUE!
THIS IS AN OUTRAGE!
EGG CUPS
HA! HA! HA!
THANKS FOR THE EGG CUPS, SNOOTY! NOW YOU CAN HAVE THE FRUIT!
HOWL
HELP
EGG CUPS
HELP! WOW! STOP THROWING BANANA SKINS!
SLAP
HAVE A PLUM STONE, SNITCHY! THEY'RE FREE!
PONG

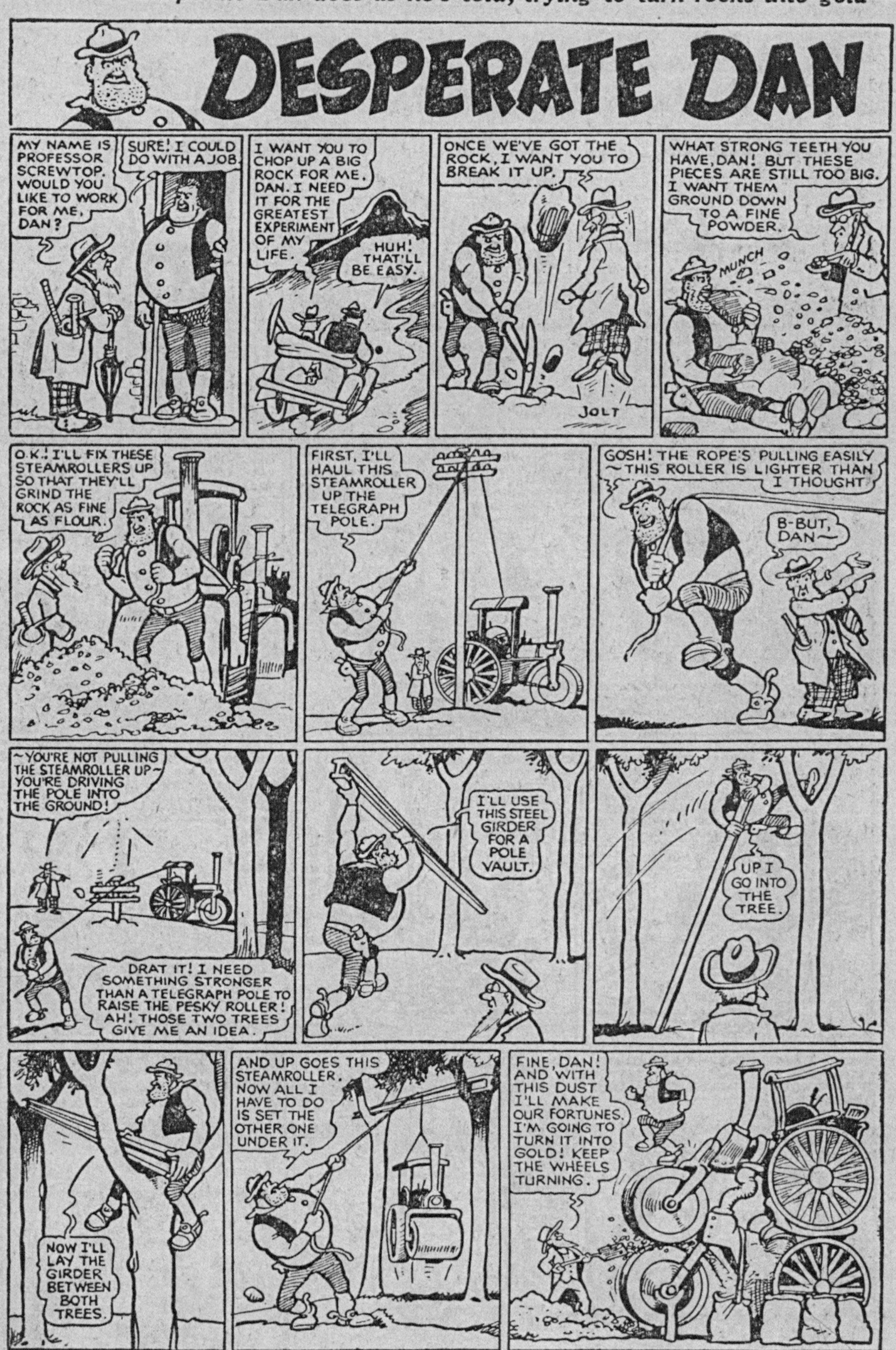
Desperate Dan does as he's told, trying to turn rocks into gold —
DESPERATE DAN
MY NAME IS PROFESSOR SCREWTOP. WOULD YOU LIKE TO WORK FOR ME, DAN?
SURE! I COULD DO WITH A JOB.
I WANT YOU TO CHOP UP A BIG ROCK FOR ME, DAN. I NEED IT FOR THE GREATEST EXPERIMENT OF MY LIFE.
HUH! THAT'LL BE EASY.
ONCE WE'VE GOT THE ROCK, I WANT YOU TO BREAK IT UP.
JOLT
WHAT STRONG TEETH YOU HAVE, DAN! BUT THESE PIECES ARE STILL TOO BIG. I WANT THEM GROUND DOWN TO A FINE POWDER.
MUNCH
O.K.! I'LL FIX THESE STEAMROLLERS UP SO THAT THEY'LL GRIND THE ROCK AS FINE AS FLOUR.
FIRST, I'LL HAUL THIS STEAMROLLER UP THE TELEGRAPH POLE.
GOSH! THE ROPE'S PULLING EASILY —THIS ROLLER IS LIGHTER THAN I THOUGHT.
B-BUT, DAN—
—YOU'RE NOT PULLING THE STEAMROLLER UP—YOU'RE DRIVING THE POLE INTO THE GROUND!
DRAT IT! I NEED SOMETHING STRONGER THAN A TELEGRAPH POLE TO RAISE THE PESKY ROLLER! AH! THOSE TWO TREES GIVE ME AN IDEA.
I'LL USE THIS STEEL GIRDER FOR A POLE VAULT.
UP I GO INTO THE TREE.
NOW I'LL LAY THE GIRDER BETWEEN BOTH TREES.
AND UP GOES THIS STEAMROLLER. NOW ALL I HAVE TO DO IS SET THE OTHER ONE UNDER IT.
FINE, DAN! AND WITH THIS DUST I'LL MAKE OUR FORTUNES. I'M GOING TO TURN IT INTO GOLD! KEEP THE WHEELS TURNING.

—When his partner's plans are beaten, all the rocks by Dan are eaten!
He chews rocks and spits dust— and the cakes he eats are all crust!
IN SCREWTOP'S LABORATORY
NOW THIS SPECIAL CHEMICAL SHOULD TURN THE STONE PASTE TO GOLD.
POOF
WOW!
GOSH, PROFESSOR, IT WORKS! HERE'S A GOLD COIN.
I DIDN'T MAKE THAT. IT'S THE LUCKY COIN I WEAR ON MY WATCH CHAIN! HELP ME OUT OF THIS MESS!
JUMPING COYOTES! IS THAT YOU, PROFESSOR?
I'LL CHIP YOU FREE. SAY, PROFESSOR, YOU SURE HAVE CHANGED. WHAT A FUNNY FACE YOU HAVE NOW.
THAT'S NOT MY FACE, YOU IDIOT, IT'S MY BOOTS! MY FACE IS DOWN HERE. I'M STANDING ON MY HEAD!
O.K.! I'LL STAND YOU THE RIGHT WAY UP! THERE, THAT'S CRACKED ALL THE ROCK OFF YOU!
WOW
HELP
OOH
WE'LL TRY AGAIN. I MUST HAVE ADDED THE WRONG CHEMICAL LAST TIME. I'LL MAKE THESE HEAPS INTO SOLID NUGGETS OF GOLD WHEN I ADD THE PROPER CHEMICAL.
THERE, THAT'S DONE. NOW THE TRAY MUST GET AN ELECTRICAL CHARGE OF 1,400,001 VOLTS. JUST CLIP THOSE WIRES ON, DAN.
YOU SHOULD HAVE LET GO BEFORE I PULLED THE SWITCH! DON'T LAUGH, IT'S NOT FUNNY!
HO-HO-HO! I CAN'T HELP IT! THIS PESKY ELECTRICITY IS TICKLING ME!
ALAS! I AM A FAILURE. I HAVE NOT DISCOVERED HOW TO CHANGE STONE INTO GOLD.
SNIFF—THESE LUMPS SMELL GOOD. THEY'VE GONE QUITE HARD.
YOU HAVEN'T MADE GOLD, PROF, BUT THESE ARE THE BEST ROCK CAKES I'VE TASTED.
TRY ONE!
CLONK
THAT NIGHT IN DAN'S BEDROOM
THAT ELECTRIC SHOCK HAS MADE ME LIGHT UP LIKE A LAMP—AND I SURE AM ENJOYING THE PROF'S ROCK CAKES!
CHEW

YOW-WOW
SHAGGY DOGGY
OH DEAR! THERE GOES A FIVE POUND NOTE!
£5
PLONK!
YOU ARE A CLEVER DOG!
I'M PROFESSOR WARBLE. AS A REWARD I'LL TEACH YOU HOW TO SING!
YAP YAP
CARRY ON LIKE THAT AND YOU'LL SOON BE A STAR SINGING DOG!
YELP-YAP YAP YAP
?
WOW-WOW
YAP-YAP YELP!
OUT YOU GO AND SING SOME-WHERE ELSE!
BROADCASTING STATION
STUDIO
NOW I'LL SWITCH ON THE WIRELESS AND HEAR SOME REAL SINGING.
YOU WILL NOW HEAR SHAGGY THE SINGING DOG!
NO!
YAP-YAP WUFF-WUFF YELP!
A.M.

A laugh tale of your favourite funsters, the metal maid and the brassbound butler.

TIN LIZZIE was hard at work, scrubbing the floor of her master's kitchen. Professor Puffin was a lucky man having two mechanical servants to do all his housework for him. Besides Tin Lizzie, who did all the washing, ironing and cooking, there was Brassribs, the automatic butler. His duties were to serve the Professor's meals and look after his clothes. At this moment Brassribs was in the dining-room, serving breakfast to the Professor—or so Tin Lizzie thought as she scrubbed the floor just behind the kitchen door.

2—In fact, Brassribs had finished serving the Professor and was about to enter the kitchen. Both his hands were fully occupied holding a tray, and the only way he could open the door was by kicking it ! *Crash !* The door thumped against Lizzie, and the metal maid took a nose-dive into the bucket of soapy water she had been using.

3—" Haw ! Haw !" Brassribs bellowed. " It's about time your face had a wash !" Lizzie jerked her head from the bucket and charged towards the butler, brandishing the scrubbing brush. Brassribs promptly beat it. Out into the street he charged, and here Lizzie came within throwing range. *Clang !* The brush struck the butler's iron dome.

What is the difference between a fisherman and a truant?

4—Brassribs looked hurriedly round to see how far ahead of Lizzie he was, and he didn't notice the ladder in front of him. Down it came, and down came the sweep who was on it. He thudded on top of the metal maid.

5—" Oh !" he groaned. " My back ! I can't do my work now." Professor Puffin dashed out to help the sweep to his feet. " Don't worry, my man," he said. " My servants will manage to do your job for you."

6—So Tin Lizzie and Brassribs set off to sweep the chimneys which the sweep had been about to tackle. Between them they made light work of pulling the barrow.

7—They both thought chimney-sweeping would be an easy job. But, at the very first house, the brush jammed in the chimney. " I can't move it," Lizzie hooted.

8—" I'll go up on the roof and push something down the chimney to free the brush," Brassribs rumbled. Off he went. Armed with the longest clothes prop he could find he climbed up the sweep's ladder to the roof.

9—" Now which chimney is it?" he muttered. He prodded cautiously down each chimney until he felt the clothes prop strike something solid. " Found it !" he boomed, and thrust the prop hard downwards.

One baits his hooks, the other hates his books.

10—There was plenty of power behind that thrust of the butler's. Lizzie was tugging frantically in an attempt to pull the brush down when—*Thud!* The butler's heave sent the brush handle whacking into her tummy.

11—The metal maid was hurled across the room. But she picked herself up in a flash. "So! A funny man!" she grated. "I'll fix him!" Grabbing the brush handle, she charged at top speed towards the fireplace.

12—*Wheee!* The brush fairly whistled up the chimney. Nothing could stop it this time, so fierce was Lizzie's charge, and the sooty end smacked Brassribs on the chin.

13—Brassribs felt himself falling. He grabbed the chimney pot, but it broke loose. Down he clattered. And a policeman got in the way of the falling chimney pot!

14—This was just the chance that Smash-and-Grab Bert had been wanting. Brassribs was helpless, so was the policeman, and Lizzie was helping the bobby. No one could stop Bert smashing a jeweller's window.

15—Then he made off with as much as he could carry, stepping on the helpless Brassribs on the way. That was going to prove his undoing. Lizzie noticed the sooty footprint on the butler's white shirt-front.

What is taken before you get it? — Your photograph.

16—"Look!" she hooted. "If we can find somebody with a footprint to match that, we'll have caught the crook. Come on, Rustyribs." The dazed butler hurried off with Lizzie on her search for the crook.

17—Every man the metal servants met was grabbed and, in spite of his protests, had his right foot held against the sooty mark on the butler's chest. The first dozen men were all innocent. It seemed a hopeless quest.

18—But they searched so long that they were bound to come up with their quarry in the end. He fought in vain to escape their clutches. His foot matched the footprint, and Smash-and-Grab Bert was nabbed.

19—"To the police station with him!" Brassribs rumbled. The police were glad to see Bert. They'd been keeping a cell for him for a long time! He was marched off, and a reward was handed to the metal servants.

20—"Excellent!" boomed Brassribs. "I can buy a new shirt-front." "No, you don't!" Lizzie objected. "We're going to make up for the trouble we've given the sweep." Brassribs rumbled angrily, but all the same he helped Lizzie to prepare a party for the sweep's big family. Never had there been a gayer party. Even the bold Brassribs had the time of his life.

BRASSNECK
WATCH OUT, BRASSNECK! I NEARLY MADE YOU DROP A TOMATO THERE!
NONSENSE, CHARLEY! MY ELECTRIC WORKS ALWAYS MOVE FASTER THAN YOU CAN!
CHUCKLER Charley Brand is the luckiest schoolboy in the world. He's the only lad whose best pal is made of metal! And what a pal he is! Although he is constructed of tin and steel, brass and copper, and his innards are stuffed full of electric works, Brassneck can do tricks that no ordinary schoolboy can do.
Like this one, for instance—juggling half a dozen tomatoes while at the same time riding Charley's bike backwards!
No wonder Charley is the envy of his chums.

But Charley's Dad was not impressed. In fact, Mr Brand was hopping mad.
HOI! WHERE DID YOU GET THESE TOMATOES?
ER—IN THE GREENHOUSE, DAD!
YOU HOOLIGANS! THESE ARE SOME OF MY BEST TOMATOES ENTERED FOR THE MAYOR'S PRIZE!

And Dad had something else to complain about.
AND ANOTHER THING—I THOUGHT I TOLD YOU TO CUT THE GRASS LAST WEEK!

Brassneck had a flash of inspiration! He removed the front wheel of Charley's bike and replaced it with the lawnmower. A man watched suspiciously. It was the nasty next-door neighbour, Crabby Crabtree.
ONE MORE TURN OF THE SPANNER, CHARLEY, AND I'LL BE READY TO START.
YOU'RE A MARVEL, BRASSNECK!

Crabby had also entered for the Mayor's prize and he was envious of Dad's tomatoes.
BRAND'S TOMATOES LOOK MUCH BIGGER THAN MINE. WHAT CAN I DO TO SPOIL HIS LOT?

Old Sandy, the retired coal horse, was grazing in a nearby field—and surprisingly enough, he liked tomatoes. Crabby lured the animal along with a few of his own.
COME ON THEN, YOU SCRUFFY OLD NAG, MAKE UP YOUR MIND—DO YOU WANT THEM OR DON'T YOU? I'M NOT STANDING HERE ALL DAY!

Sandy liked the juicy taste. So much so, that when Crabby laid a trail of tomatoes up to Dad Brand's greenhouse door, the horse gobbled them eagerly.
HEH-HEH! THIS IS WORKING BETTER THAN I EXPECTED!

When he reached the greenhouse door and saw the wealth of bigger and better tomatoes ahead of him, Old Sandy's greedy eyes widened.

Seconds later, Brassneck came buzzing along on his mechanised lawnmower. He almost fell off in astonishment when he spotted the horse in the greenhouse.
OH, MY GOODNESS! HOW DID THAT HORSE GET IN THERE?

THE INTERFERING TIN-CAN FREAK!
GET OUT OF THERE, YOU GREEDY BEAST!
Sandy refused to budge. Brassneck had to shove about a ton of horseflesh out of the greenhouse.
Through a peephole in the fence, Crabby watched in dismay.

YAHOO!
Old Sandy was annoyed at being removed from his bean-feast, and he lashed out with his hindlegs. His heavy hoofs smashed the fence to smithereens—and flattened Crabby at the same time.
WOW! THIS IS A HOT HANDFUL!

But Crabby didn't stay down. He still meant to put paid to those super tomatoes.
THIS EXTRA STRONG WEED-KILLER WILL DO FOR THEM!
POWER X WEED KILLER

With a long pair of pincers, the scally-wag reached through a hole in the patched-up fence and dropped lumps of the powerful weed-killer into Charley's Dad's watering can.
THAT'S THE CAN OLD BRAND USES FOR WATERING HIS TOMATOES!
TWO BIG LUMPS AND THEN ONE MORE FOR THE POT—HEH-HEH!

But Crabby's second plan went wrong, too! Brassneck's works were red-hot from his mowing exertions, and he took a mighty swig from the watering can to cool them down.
I HOPE THIS WATER IS DEAD COLD!
GRACIOUS ME! I HOPE I MADE THAT MIXTURE STRONG ENOUGH!

GROOGH!
CRUMBS! IF ANY OF THAT SPRAY LANDS ON ME, MY CLOTHES WILL BE BURNT OFF MY BACK!
SPLUTTER! What a horrible taste! Brassneck spat out the filthy liquid in a great jet which shot across the fence and sprayed over Crabby's rose-bed.

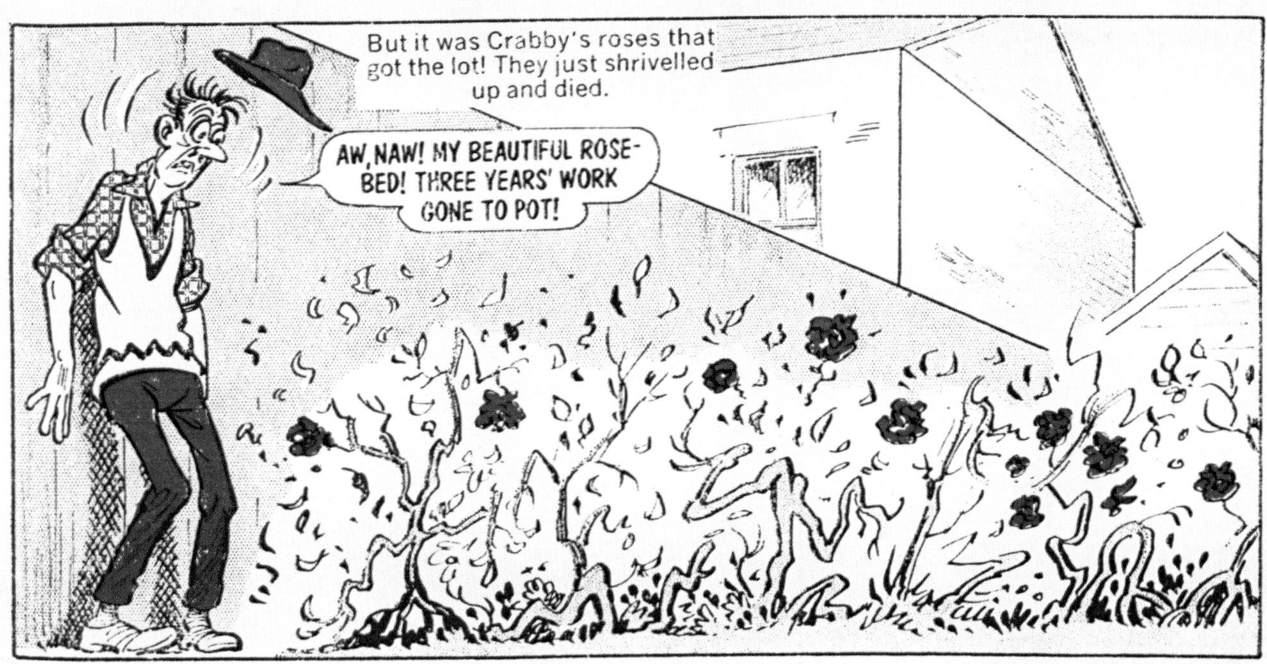
But it was Crabby's roses that got the lot! They just shrivelled up and died.
AW, NAW! MY BEAUTIFUL ROSE-BED! THREE YEARS' WORK GONE TO POT!

Now that the lawn was neatly mown, Charley and Brassneck fancied a game of cricket.
BAGS ME TO BAT FIRST!
THAT'S OKAY! I'LL SOON BOWL YOU ANYWAY!

Meanwhile, over the fence, Crabby Crabtree had thought up another beastly scheme.
JUST WAIT TILL THIS LITTLE LOT GET AMONG BRAND'S TOMATOES! THERE WON'T BE EVEN A LEAF LEFT!

Carefully Crabby pushed the box of insects into his pocket.
WHY DIDN'T I THINK OF THIS BEFORE?

The branches of a tree in Crabby's garden conveniently overhung Mr Brand's greenhouse. Now the villain shinned up into this tree.
THIS IS A GOOGLY, BRASSNECK!
I'D BETTER WATCH THESE BRATS DON'T SEE ME!

WHACK! Batsman Brassneck belted Charley's googly ball straight towards the tree.
GOSH, I'VE HIT THAT ONE TOO HARD!

Crabby was creeping along a branch when the ball smacked against his trouser pocket—smashing the box in it with amazing results.
AARGH! ALL THOSE INSECTS ARE LOOSE IN MY PANTS!

Crabby began to scratch himself so feverishly that he lost his grip on the tree. PLONK! He plummeted to the ground.
OOYAH!
AARGH!
OOYAH!
EEK!
OOF!

It took Crabby quite some time to get over that disaster, but in the end he climbed up the tree again, this time armed with a hose.
I'M NOT GIVING UP YET!

Crabby pushed the nozzle in through the skylight window of Dad Brand's green-house, and a torrent of water cascaded down on the tomato plants.
HURRAH! SUCCESS AT LAST! KING ROBERT THE BRUCE WAS RIGHT—TRY, TRY AND TRY AGAIN!
It was the noise of rushing water that eventually brought Dad Brand running to investigate.
WHAT ON EARTH! ALL THE SOIL HAS BEEN WASHED OUT OF THE TOMATO BOXES! I'LL SLAY THE VANDAL WHO DID THIS!

Brassneck reached for the hose and gave it a tremendous jerk—snapping it!
I NEED ONLY ONE GUESS TO KNOW WHERE THAT HOSE CAME FROM?

Meanwhile, in Crabby's garden, the Mayor and his judges had arrived to inspect Crabby's tomatoes.
Water from the broken hose suddenly sprayed all over the visitors.
WELL, MR CRABTREE! THEY'RE THE BEST WE'VE SEEN SO FAR! AARGH!
BEAUTIES AREN'T THEY?

The Mayor and his judges thought it was a Crabby trick, and they disqualified him on the spot.
I'VE NEVER BEEN SO INSULTED IN ALL MY LIFE! LET US BE OFF, GENTLEMEN!
QUITE RIGHT, YOUR WORSHIP. DISQUALIFY HIM FOR LIFE!
I'M EVER SO SORRY, YOUR WORSHIP! I CAN EXPLAIN—ER—OR CAN I?

The judges duly arrived to inspect Mr Brand's tomatoes and they were most impressed.
I SAY! THESE ARE STUPENDOUS! THEY'RE THE BEST TOMATOES I HAVE EVER SEEN!
AND THEY TASTE JOLLY GOOD, TOO!

Needless to say, Dad Brand proved the winner, and that evening, a celebration party was held. But Mr Brand might not have been so successful if it hadn't been for Charley's remarkable metal pal, Brassneck.
YES! ANOTHER CUP, PLEASE!
I SAY—YOU'D NEVER BELIEVE WHAT HAPPENED TO US THIS AFTERNOON—A RUFFIAN ACTUALLY SQUIRTED US WITH A HOSE—
GRR!
1ST PRIZE
HOLD THAT POSE FOR A SECOND, MR BRAND, AND SAY 'CHEESE'.

"Use your loaf!" says Korky Cat—And here you see how he did that!
KORKY
THE CAT
HOW AM I GOING TO DRAG THESE LOGS UP THE HILL AND HOIST THEM ON TO MY LORRY WITHOUT A CRANE?
TIMBER
HEY, WAIT— I MIGHT BE ABLE TO HELP YOU.
ROYAL AIR FORCE WEATHER STATION
THEY'LL HAVE WHAT I WANT HERE!
COULD YOU LEND ME A COUPLE OF WEATHER BALLOONS AND A PAIR OF DIVER'S BOOTS, PLEASE?
OF COURSE, KORKY— DELIGHTED!
LOW
GET THESE BOOTS ON, KORKY, WHILE I FETCH THE BALLOONS.
I'LL COME BACK FOR THE OTHER ONE.
STORES
GOOD SHOW!
THERE YOU ARE, SAM— ONE LOG HOISTED!
WELL, I'M BLOWED!

What shoots out of the ground at 120 m.p.h.?
A GREAT IDEA OF YOURS, KORKY!
WE'LL SOON HAVE THE LORRY LOADED NOW!
TIMBE
I'LL BE BACK FOR MORE IN AN HOUR, KORKY!
PHEW! NOW I CAN HAVE A REST!
I'LL TAKE OFF THESE HEAVY BOOTS AND EASE MY FEET.
PRESENTLY
I'M BACK, KORKY!
RIGHT! NEXT ONE COMING UP!
BUT WHAT ABOUT THOSE BOOTS?
READY? GRAB HOLD OF THE FIRST BALLOON.
RIGHT— I'VE GOT IT, SAM!
WHOOOOSH

An E-type Carrot, or an Austin Healey Sprout!

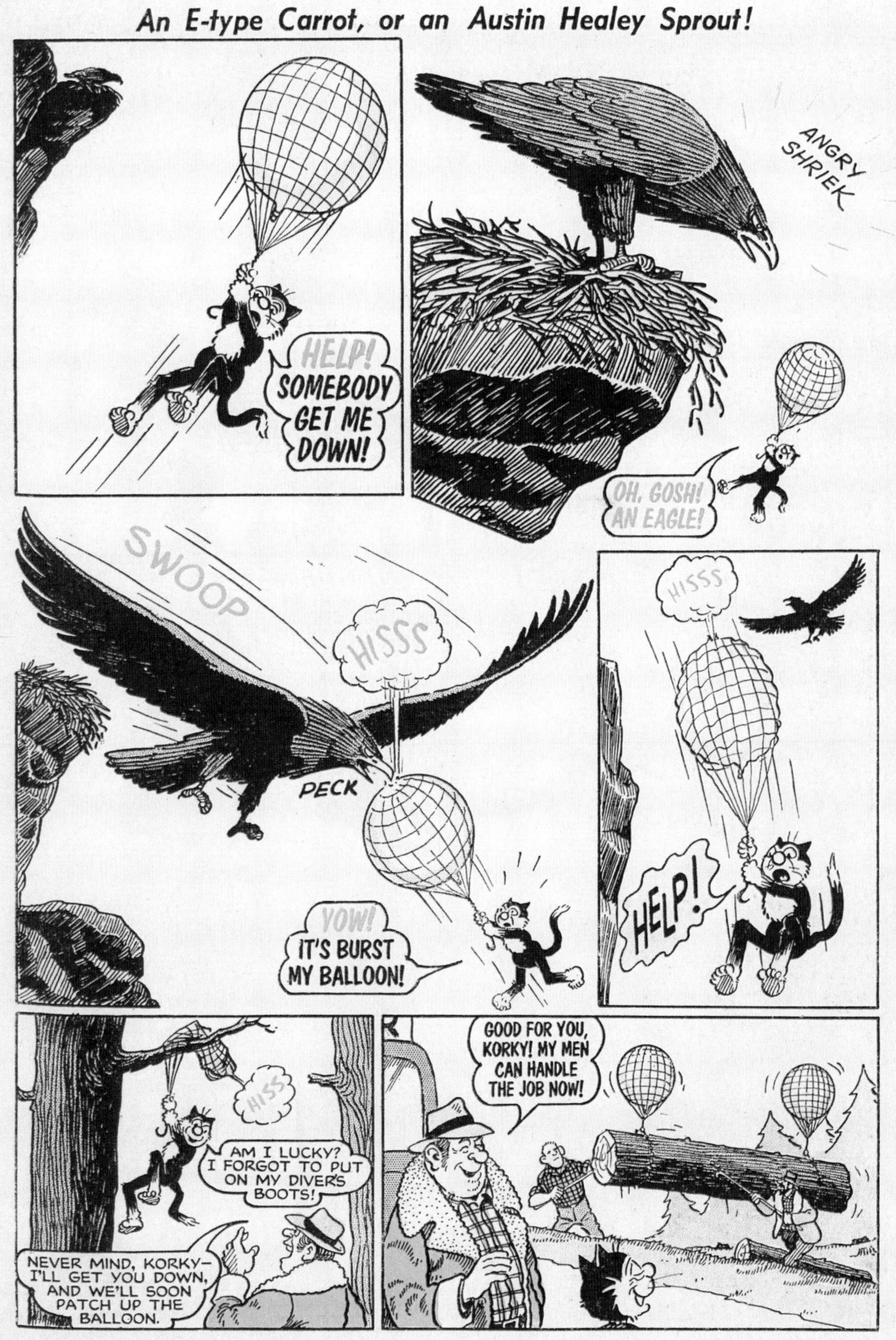

What kind of tie would a hog wear?—A pig sty! (pig's tie).
RIGHT, CAST OFF!
HOPE YOU REMEMBERED TO GET THEM DIVER'S BOOTS, SAM—
WHOOOOSH
WHOOOOSH
OH, NO, I FORGOT!
SWOOP
HELP!
HOW WILL WE GET THEM DOWN, KORKY?
OH, THEY'LL COME DOWN FOR SURE!
QUICK! THAT EAGLE HAS BURST THEIR BALLOONS! GET UNDER THEM, SAM, AND BREAK THEIR FALL!
YOW!
OUCH!
CRASH
THAT WAS TOUGH LUCK! WHERE'S THE NEAREST HOSPITAL?

Winker WATSON
MY THIRD-FORMERS REALLY ENJOY THEMSELVES WATCHING THE GO-KART RACING ON TELEVISION, DON'T THEY, HEADMASTER?
YES, MR CREEP, AND IT KEEPS THEM OUT OF MISCHIEF, TOO!
NOTICE
GREYTOWERS SCHOOL
TELEVISION ROOM
* GO-KART * MEETING
GOLLY! ISN'T IT EXCITING, TROTTY?
NOT HALF, WINKER!
WINKER WATSON and his pals of the Third Form at Greytowers were halfway out of their seats with excitement. The thrills and spills of go-kart racing held them spellbound, and there wasn't a boy among them who wouldn't have swopped his back teeth for a go at driving one of them
When the TV programme ended, the room buzzed with talk, and out of all the chatter a great idea was born. The upshot was that Winker led a deputation on a visit to his Form Master

Winker had a favour to ask, and his pals were there to back him up.
PLEASE, MR CREEP, SIR. COULD MY PALS AND I HAVE A GO AT BUILDING A GO-KART FOR OURSELVES?
DON'T BE RIDICULOUS, WATSON! THE ONLY THING YOU LOT COULD MAKE IS A MISTAKE—AND YOU'RE MAKING ONE NOW IF YOU THINK THE SCHOOL IS GOING TO PAY FOR A HARE-BRAINED SCHEME LIKE THAT!
Winker wasn't known as the star wangler of Greytowers for nothing. And something he spotted an hour or so later set his wily brain-box working.
THERE'S CREEPY PUTTING HIS ROTTEN CAR AWAY, TROTTY. I HOPE HE DOESN'T STOP AND GOES SLAP INTO HIS OLD MOTOR BIKE...... HEY, THAT GIVES ME AN IDEA!
NEXT MORNING
It was well before breakfast when the sound of Creepy's car horn brought the Third Formers to the windows of their dormitory.
TOOT!
OLD CREEPY'S GOING OUT EARLY THIS MORNING, WINKER!
AND HE'LL BE GONE ALL DAY, TOO, LADS! I SENT HIM A TELEGRAM OFFERING HIM A HEADMASTER'S JOB—200 MILES AWAY!
HURRY UP! LET'S GET DRESSED AND GET CRACKING IN HIS GARAGE!
This was the reason Winker wanted his Form Master out of the way. He wanted to raid Creepy's garage!
RIGHT! TROTTY AND I WILL STRIP THE BIKE DOWN, WHILE TWO OF YOU NIP OFF TO THE SCRAP YARD IN TOWN AND SEE IF YOU CAN GET FOUR OLD SCOOTER WHEELS. AND SOMEBODY GET AN OLD BEDSTEAD FROM THE SCHOOL STORE!
TOOLS

OH, MY GOODNESS! WHILE I'VE BEEN AWAY ON THAT WILD GOOSE CHASE, SOME SCOUNDREL HAS STOLEN THE ENGINE OF MY MOTOR-CYCLE!
Creepy was furious when he returned – and what he found in his garage didn't help his temper at all!
A glimmer of suspicion entered Creepy's mind when he looked up at a lighted window.
THAT'S FUNNY! THE LIGHT IS ON IN THE METALWORK ROOM.
But if Creepy thought he would find his missing engine here, he was wrong.
WATSON! YOU BOYS! WHAT ON EARTH ARE YOU DOING IN HERE AT THIS TIME OF NIGHT?
HANDICRAFT AND METALWORK ROOM
HOW'S THAT, SIR?
T. TROTT
ONLY MAKING NAMEPLATES FOR OURSELVES, MR CREEP, SIR! LOOK AT THE ONE TROTTY'S DONE, SIR! ISN'T IT A BEAUTY?
But Creepy's suspicions would really have been aroused if he had seen the name on Winker's nameplate!
CREEPY'S GONE NOW, WINKER. LET'S HAVE A LOOK AT THE SPECIAL NAMEPLATE YOU'VE BEEN MAKING.
THE CREEPY SCORCHER
THERE IT IS, LADS, AND NOW LET'S FINISH THE WORK!
And here was the Creepy Scorcher itself. It had been cunningly hoisted up among the roof beams and concealed from the short-sighted master by a big sheet.
GOOD JOB WE HEARD CREEPY COMING. WE DON'T WANT HIM TO SEE THE CREEPY SCORCHER TOO SOON!
LOWER AWAY, LADS!

NEXT MORNING
VROOM! SPLUTTER!
Creepy was startled by a throaty roar—and what's more he recognised the noise at once!
EEEK! THAT'S MY MOTOR-BIKE ENGINE —I'D KNOW THE SOUND OF IT A MILE AWAY!
It was at least a mile away by the time the master got out after it!
I'M GETTING NEAR IT AT LAST—THE SOUND IS COMING FROM THAT FIELD OVER THERE!
VROOM! VROOM!
GOOD GRIEF! IT'S WATSON! I SAY, STOP AT ONCE!
What a shock for Creepy when he saw the Kart! He yelled to Winker—but the wangler couldn't hear because of the roar of the engine.
VROOM!
THE CREEPY SCORCHER
As Winker opened the throttle, Creepy set off in pursuit.
HEY! THAT'S MY BIKE YOU'VE PINCHED, MR CREEP, SIR!
GUR! JUST WAIT TILL I CATCH UP WITH HIM!
WHOOPS! THAT'S TORN IT! CREEPY'S CAUGHT UP WITH ME!
GOOD! WATSON'S SKIDDED AND FALLEN OFF! NOW I'LL GET HIM!
Winker's idea had been to lure Creepy into this muddy corner, then make him come a cropper. But the wangler had been a little too smart!

Things looked black for Winker. He was cornered, and there seemed no way out.
ON YOUR FEET, WATSON, AND YOU'LL PAY DEARLY FOR THIS....
OO-ER! YES SIR, MR CREEP!

But just as Creepy was about to rebuke him, an unexpected interruption saved the wangler's bacon.
HEY, I SAY, MR CREEP! I MUST CONGRATULATE YOU AND YOUR BOYS ON SUCH A SPLENDID IDEA! I'M MR FIPPS FROM CLIFFEND SCHOOL. DON'T PUNISH THAT BOY FOR UPSETTING YOUR WONDERFUL INVENTION. I'M SURE HE COULDN'T HELP IT!

ER...OF COURSE, MR FIPPS, SIR. WE COULDN'T HAVE MADE IT IF GOOD OLD MR CREEP HADN'T GIVEN US HIS MOTOR-BIKE ENGINE!
AHEM! DON'T MENTION IT, WATSON, LAD!
Winker was quick to hand out some credit to Creepy, knowing that this was the best way to get round the master.
GOOD FOR YOU, MR CREEP, AND NOW HOW ABOUT LETTING YOUNG WATSON DEMONSTRATE YOUR SPLENDID GO-KART FOR ME?

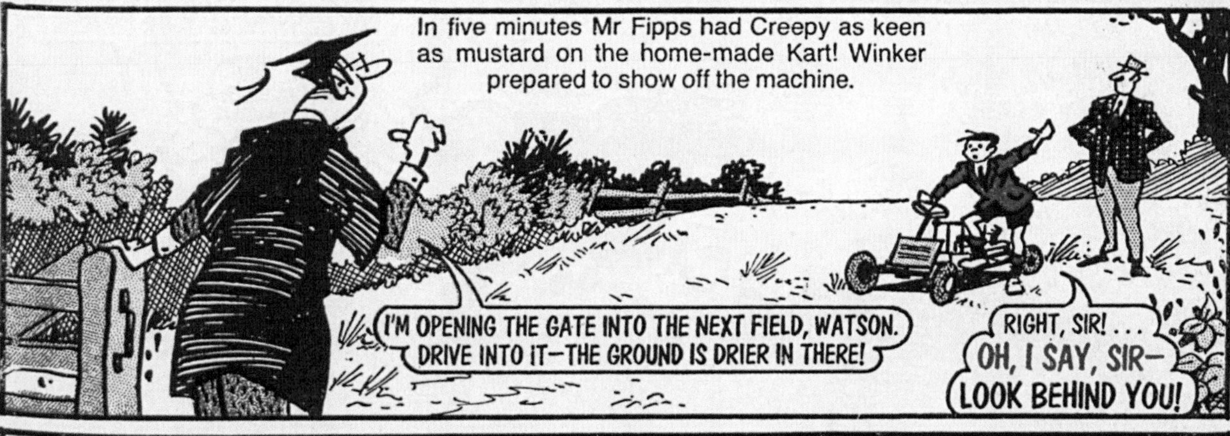
In five minutes Mr Fipps had Creepy as keen as mustard on the home-made Kart! Winker prepared to show off the machine.
I'M OPENING THE GATE INTO THE NEXT FIELD, WATSON. DRIVE INTO IT—THE GROUND IS DRIER IN THERE!
RIGHT, SIR! ... OH, I SAY, SIR—LOOK BEHIND YOU!

Creepy was short-sighted, but this snorting monster was so close behind him that he could see the whites of its eyes turning red!
SNORT!
EEEK! IT'S A B-BULL!

The bull charged, and Creepy bolted. But Winker saw that, unless something was done, the master would be caught inside a few yards.
I'LL MAKE A RUN FOR IT...
OWCH! MY ANKLE! I'VE TWISTED IT!
SNORT!
IT'S GAINING ON HIM, WATSON!
QUICK! GIVE ME A SHOVE TO START UP, SIR!
HE'S DONE IT! HE'S GOT BETWEEN CREEP AND THE BULL! QUICK THINKING, WATSON!
VROOM!
OO-ER!
CREEPY SCORCHER
The bull sheered off, scared by the roar of the Kart engine.
Then Winker drove the beast back the way it had come, using a stick and the roar of the engine to herd it along.
YOU'RE SAFE, MR CREEP! WATSON'S GOT EVERYTHING UNDER CONTROL!
YAH! BACK INTO YOUR OWN FIELD YOU BRUTE!
OO! MY ANKLE! I CAN'T MOVE!
PANIC OVER, EVERYBODY! THE BULL'S BACK WHERE HE BELONGS!
HEY, YOU OTHER BOYS! FIND SOME KIND OF STRETCHER FOR MR CREEP—HE'LL HAVE TO BE CARRIED!
OO! IT'S AGONY, MR FIPPS!
While Winker secured the gate, Creepy lay and moaned, so sorry for himself that he didn't think of thanking the lad who had saved him.

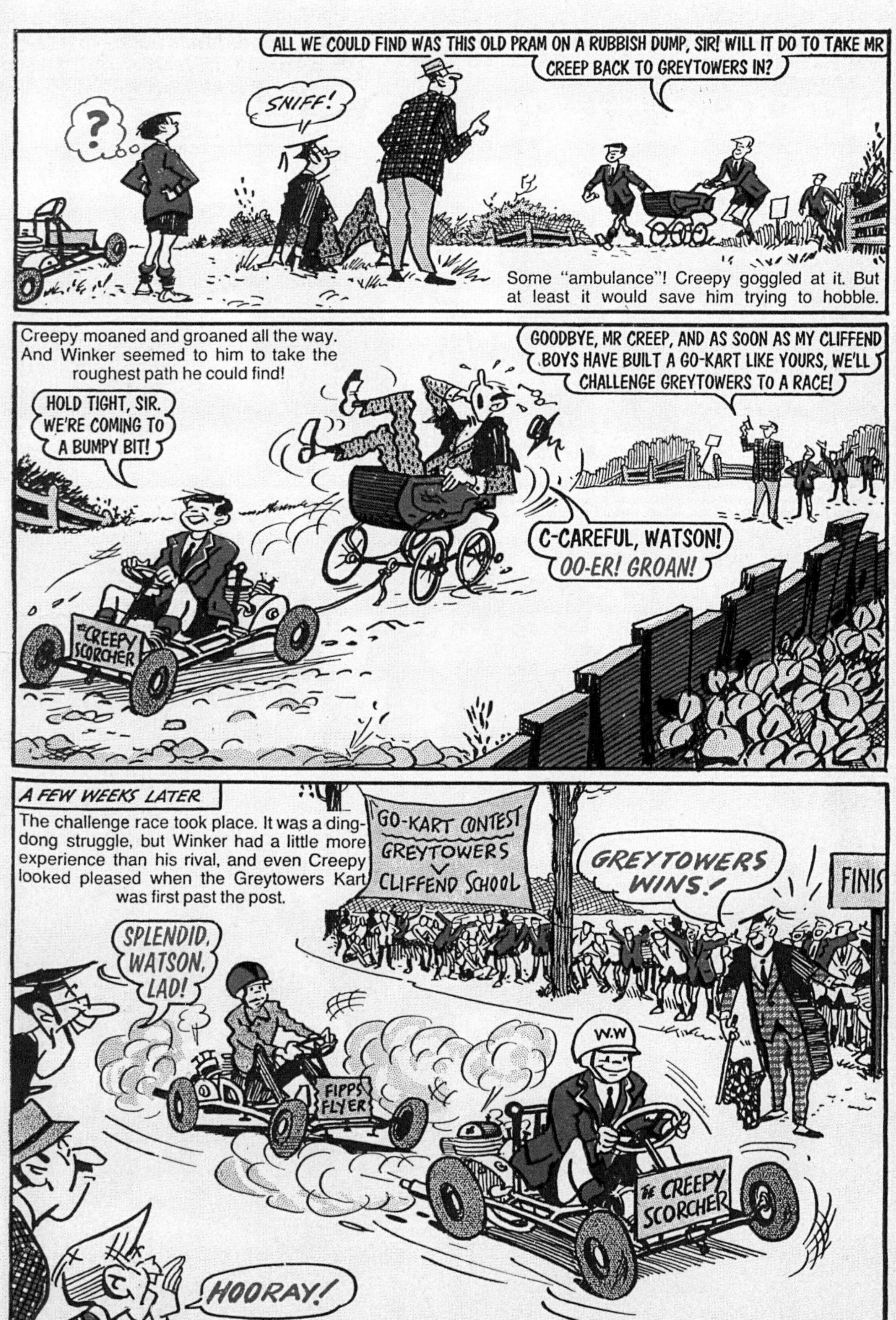
ALL WE COULD FIND WAS THIS OLD PRAM ON A RUBBISH DUMP, SIR! WILL IT DO TO TAKE MR CREEP BACK TO GREYTOWERS IN?
?
SNIFF!
Some "ambulance"! Creepy goggled at it. But at least it would save him trying to hobble.
Creepy moaned and groaned all the way. And Winker seemed to him to take the roughest path he could find!
GOODBYE, MR CREEP, AND AS SOON AS MY CLIFFEND BOYS HAVE BUILT A GO-KART LIKE YOURS, WE'LL CHALLENGE GREYTOWERS TO A RACE!
HOLD TIGHT, SIR. WE'RE COMING TO A BUMPY BIT!
C-CAREFUL, WATSON! OO-ER! GROAN!
THE CREEPY SCORCHER
A FEW WEEKS LATER
The challenge race took place. It was a ding-dong struggle, but Winker had a little more experience than his rival, and even Creepy looked pleased when the Greytowers Kart was first past the post.
GO-KART CONTEST GREYTOWERS V CLIFFEND SCHOOL
GREYTOWERS WINS!
FINIS
SPLENDID, WATSON, LAD!
W.W
FIPPS FLYER
THE CREEPY SCORCHER
HOORAY!

But the smile vanished from Creepy's face a few minutes later, when the Headmaster made the presentation to the winner.
...AND IT GIVES ME GREAT PLEASURE TO PRESENT THE WINNER WITH THE CLARENCE CREEP SILVER CUP FOR GO-KART RACING!
BETTER LUCK NEXT TIME, CLIFFEND!
HOORAY! GOOD OLD WINKER!
GOLLY! THANK YOU, HEADMASTER, SIR!
EH? THE WHAT?
MM

Creepy leaped out of his seat. Had he heard right? What had the Headmaster called that Cup?
EEEK! GULP! OO-ER! Y-YES, IT WAS, WASN'T IT, HEADMASTER?
THE CLARENCE CREEP SILVER CUP, CREEP, OLD MAN! IT WAS DELIVERED TO MY STUDY THIS MORNING, AND THEY SAID IT WAS ORDERED BY TELEPHONE. BY THE WAY, THE BILL IS MADE OUT TO YOU—£10-17-6! AND WE ALL THINK IT WAS JOLLY SPORTING OF YOU TO DO IT.
BILL
COME ON, EVERYBODY! WINKER'S GOING TO DO A LAP OF HONOUR!

?
THANKS, LADS!—AND HOW ABOUT A CHEER FOR GOOD OLD MR CREEP!
HOORAY! GOOD OLD WINKER!
BILL
THE CREEPY SCORCHER
Winker the super-wangler had done it again, and as so often before, his triumph had cost Creepy plenty!

CORPORAL CLOTT
I WANT TO TEST THIS FIRE-PROOF SUIT, CLOTT. LIGHT A FIRE ON THE PARADE GROUND.
A POOL OF PARAFFIN WILL MAKE A GOOD-GOING FIRE.
MARVELLOUS! I DON'T EVEN FEEL THE HEAT! NOTHING CAN HAPPEN TO ME.
YAHOO!
WOW! I DIDN'T NOTICE SOMEONE HAD LEFT THAT MANHOLE OPEN!
MOAN! WHAT FOOL LEFT THE COVER OFF THAT MANHOLE?
I'M GOING TO TRY AGAIN—AND I'VE MADE SURE MYSELF THAT THERE ARE NO OPEN MANHOLES!
THERE YOU ARE! STANDING IN THE VERY CENTRE OF THE FIRE AND I DON'T FEEL A THING!
LOOK OUT, SIR! THE SMOKE HAS STIRRED UP THESE WASPS.
THIS FIREPROOF SUIT GIVES PERFECT PROTECTION—WOW!
YAHOO! EEK! I'M BEING STUNG TO DEATH!

HOLD STILL FOR A MOMENT, SIR, AND I'LL DROWN THE WASPS.
WE'LL HAVE ONE LAST GO! THIS TIME LIGHT THE FIRE AWAY FROM ANYTHING ELSE, OVER NEAR THE BOUNDARY FENCE.
THIS HEAP OF LEAVES AND TWIGS WILL BURN UP QUICKLY, SIR!
GOOD! I'M SATISFIED NOW THAT THIS FIRE-PROOF SUIT GIVES COMPLETE PROTECTION.
LOOK OUT, SIR! THE GATE BEHIND YOU IS BEING BURNT DOWN, AND THERE'S A BULL IN THE FIELD!
HELP! I CAN'T RUN IN THESE HEAVY BOOTS!
YAHOO!
CRUMBS! I'LL HAVE TO DODGE, TOO!
HOPE THE COLONEL WASN'T TOO BADLY HURT BY THAT BULL.
THE COOK SENDS HIS APOLOGIES, SIR, BUT HE'S BURNT ALL THE FOOD. HIS ATTENTION WAS TAKEN UP WATCHING YOU TESTING OUT THAT FIREPROOF SUIT.
GRR!

Two battling toughs—Kettle Head and Fisty Cuffs.

BERTIE BUNCLE
AND HIS CHEMICAL UNCLE
YOU PROMISED TO CUT THE GRASS LAST WEEK, BERTIE, AND YOU DIDN'T! SO GET IT DONE NOW!
OH, ALL RIGHT, UNCLE BUNCLE!

PHEW! THE GRASS IS TOO LONG FOR THE LAWNMOWER. THERE MUST BE AN EASIER WAY!

WONDER IF THERE'S ANYTHING IN UNCLE'S LAB THAT WOULD HELP?

YUMMY! SMASHING! IT'S FAR TOO TASTY! MUNCH!
WHAT'S UP, UNCLE BUNCLE?

I'VE MADE A NEW KIND OF FOOD, BERTIE. IT'S SO TASTY I CAN'T RESIST IT MYSELF. QUICK! TAKE IT AWAY AND DESTROY IT!

I HAVE A PLAN.

I'LL SCATTER THIS STUFF ALL OVER THE LONG GRASS!

THEN I'LL INVITE SOME OF MY PALS TO TASTE IT!

. . . THEY'LL LIKE IT SO MUCH THAT THEY'LL MUNCH UP ALL THE GRASS—JUST LIKE A FLOCK OF SHEEP! HO-HO!

THERE! I THINK THE BAG IS EMPTY NOW!

WHOOPS! IT WASN'T! A COUPLE OF PELLETS HAVE DROPPED INTO MY MOUTH!

OH, BOY! IT'S ABSOLUTELY SCRUMPTIOUS! DELICIOUS! I MUST HAVE MORE!
BAH! THE BAG IS EMPTY!
BUT I KNOW WHERE I CAN FIND LOTS MORE!

IN AMONGST ALL THIS LONG GRASS! YUMMY! LOVELY! MUNCH!
WHAT ON EARTH! BERTIE'S EATING THE LAWN!

I MUST STOP HIM BEFORE HE DOES HIMSELF A MISCHIEF.

OH, BOY! WHAT A TASTY WAY TO CUT GRASS!
YOU SILLY BOY! STOP THIS AT ONCE—ER— LEAVE SOME FOR ME!

PHEW! I'M FULL!
GOSH!
WOW!
MUNCH! CHEW! DELICIOUS! WHAT A SUPER FLAVOUR THIS GRASS HAS!

BRASSNECK
CRICKET, tennis, football, any sport at all—Brassneck, the metal marvel, can play them better than any superstar. The brass boy has an electric brainbox and mechanical innards that make him walk and talk like any other boy, and he can also do lots more too.
Everyone thinks he is smashing fun—except teacher, Fredo Snodgrass. And you can find out how the metal marvel turned the grumpy master into a nervous wreck in this story—

As usual, Brassneck had gone along to school with his best pal, Charley Brand. The brass boy took up position outside the classroom window, while teacher Fredo Snodgrass made an announcement to the class.
I'M AFRAID THE SCHOOL TV SET IS BROKEN, BOYS, SO YOU CAN'T HAVE YOUR NORMAL TV LESSON. HOWEVER, YOU CAN GO OUT TO PLAY FOR THE MOMENT.
Charley hurried out to join Brassneck.
IT'S NOT LIKE FREDO TO LET US PLAY DURING SCHOOL-TIME, BRASSNECK!
I KNOW, CHARLEY!
Meanwhile inside, the rascally schoolmaster had borrowed a tea-trolley from the canteen.
THAT'S GOT RID OF THE BOYS!
NOW I CAN SNEAK OFF AND WATCH THE FOOTBALL ON THE OTHER CHANNEL!
Fredo wasn't the only one with sport on his mind.
I'LL CHALK UP A GOAL ON THIS OLD SHED.
RIGHT, CHARLEY, THEN I'LL SEE IF I CAN SCORE!
Brassneck ran up and gave the ball a mighty kick.
GOAL!
WHAT A SHOT, BRASSNECK! I DIDN'T STAND A CHANCE!
WHUMP!
The thunderbolt shot made the whole shed quiver. What a shock for Fredo because he had hidden inside that very shed to watch the football match on TV.
CLUNK!
AARGH!

Brassneck's next shot at goal was even harder.
THUD!
YIKE! I'M GETTING OUT OF HERE BEFORE THE WHOLE PLACE COLLAPSES!

Fredo loaded the television set back on the trolley, and went scuttling off in search of a quieter spot.
NOW WHERE CAN I GO?
STORE

Soon he came upon the very place.
THE OLD CLOCK TOWER! NO ONE EVER GOES UP THERE! THE CLOCK'S BEEN BROKEN FOR YEARS!

It was a long hard climb to the top, but Fredo reckoned it was worth the effort.
I WON'T BE DISTURBED UP HERE!

At that very moment, however, someone WAS disturbing the boys.
YOU KNOW THE RULES! NO FOOTBALL ALLOWED IN THE PLAYGROUND!
YES, MR JENKINS!

The bad-tempered janitor confiscated Charley's football, but the lads weren't beaten yet.
DON'T WORRY, BRASSNECK! WE CAN PLAY FOOTER WITH THIS TENNIS BALL!

As soon as Oddjob Jenkins had gone, the game restarted.
MY BALL!

And it wasn't long before Brassneck gave the small ball a big kick.
AND HE SHOOTS FOR GOAL . . . OOPS!

The ball flew skywards and the hand that stopped it belonged to no goalie, but to the school clock.

It was then that Brassneck did an amazing thing. With the aid of his special suction feet he walked straight up the wall of the clock tower.
BRASSNECK WILL SOON GET THE BALL BACK!

But retrieving the ball meant moving the hand of the clock forward. And when that hand reached the hour . . .

DONG!

The deafening din almost made Fredo jump out of his skin.
WHAT ON EARTH!

DONG!
. . . the bell sounded again . . .
OOH!
THE CLOCK'S STARTED UP! JUST MY LUCK!

Fredo grabbed the television set and galloped away from the ear-splitting racket.
DONG!
MUST GET OUT OF HERE! CAN'T STAND THAT NOISE!

He didn't stop running till he reached the very last step of the clock tower stairs.
GASP! MUST FIND SOMEWHERE ELSE TO WATCH THE MATCH!

The master headed back into the school.
SCIENCE LAB.
I SHOULD BE SAFER HERE.

The science lab was just the spot. It was empty for the present.
. . . AND JONES PASSES TO ALLEN . . .

Meanwhile, the boys decided to have a change of game. Brassneck fetched some suitable equipment from the school kitchens.
ANYONE FOR TENNIS?

The brass boy had another bright idea.
WE CAN USE THESE BINS INSTEAD OF A NET!

Soon the game was in full swing.
HOW'S THAT FOR A SMASH?

Another SMASH followed when Brassneck walloped the ball straight through the science lab window.
CRASH!
REACHED IT! ... OH, NO!
GULP! THAT'S TORN IT.

The ball whistled past Fredo's nose . . .
YOW!

. . . hit some bottles full of chemicals . . .
BUMP
HYDRO-UNLIKELY

. . . and sent them crashing into the sink.
CRASH!
TINKLE
GASP! HOPE THERE WASN'T ANYTHING DANGEROUS IN THOSE BOTTLES!

The chemicals mixed together and created a horrible pong.
GLUB!
STRONG PONG

The smell was so strong that the teacher had to move on with his TV set once again.
GASP! GULP!

Fredo was running out of places to take his telly.
SHOULD BE QUIET IN HERE!
SCHOOL KITCHEN

Meanwhile, the boys went to look in the lab for their ball.
SCIENCE LAB

They had to retreat from the nasty niff.
SCIENCE LAB
UGH! WHAT A SMELL!

No one could figure out what had happened, but the boys agreed about one thing.
LET'S GET AWAY FROM HERE BEFORE WE'RE BLAMED FOR CAUSING THAT SMELL!
GOOD THINKING, BRASSNECK. LET'S GO, LADS!

They headed for the far side of the playground, and since Fredo was nowhere to be seen, one of Charley's classmates had an idea!
FANCY A GAME OF CRICKET?
YOU BET!

Moments later, the game started, and look who was first into bat!
TRY THIS ONE FOR SIZE, BRASSNECK!

WHACK! The brass boy had no trouble hitting the ball, but the fielder wasn't first eleven material.
SCHOOL KITCHEN
CRASH!
I'VE HIT A SIX!
CRUMBS! FREDO WILL HIT US FOR SIX WHEN HE SEES THAT WINDOW!
But it was poor Fredo who was hit for six! His telly-viewing seat was right in the cricket ball's flight-path.
BONK!
UMMFF!
The boys could hardly believe their eyes when they rushed into the kitchen.
SCHOOL KITCHEN
LOOK, SIR! FREDO...ER, I MEAN, MR SNODGRASS HAS FAINTED OR SOMETHING.
HOW AWFUL! I'LL CALL AN AMBULANCE!

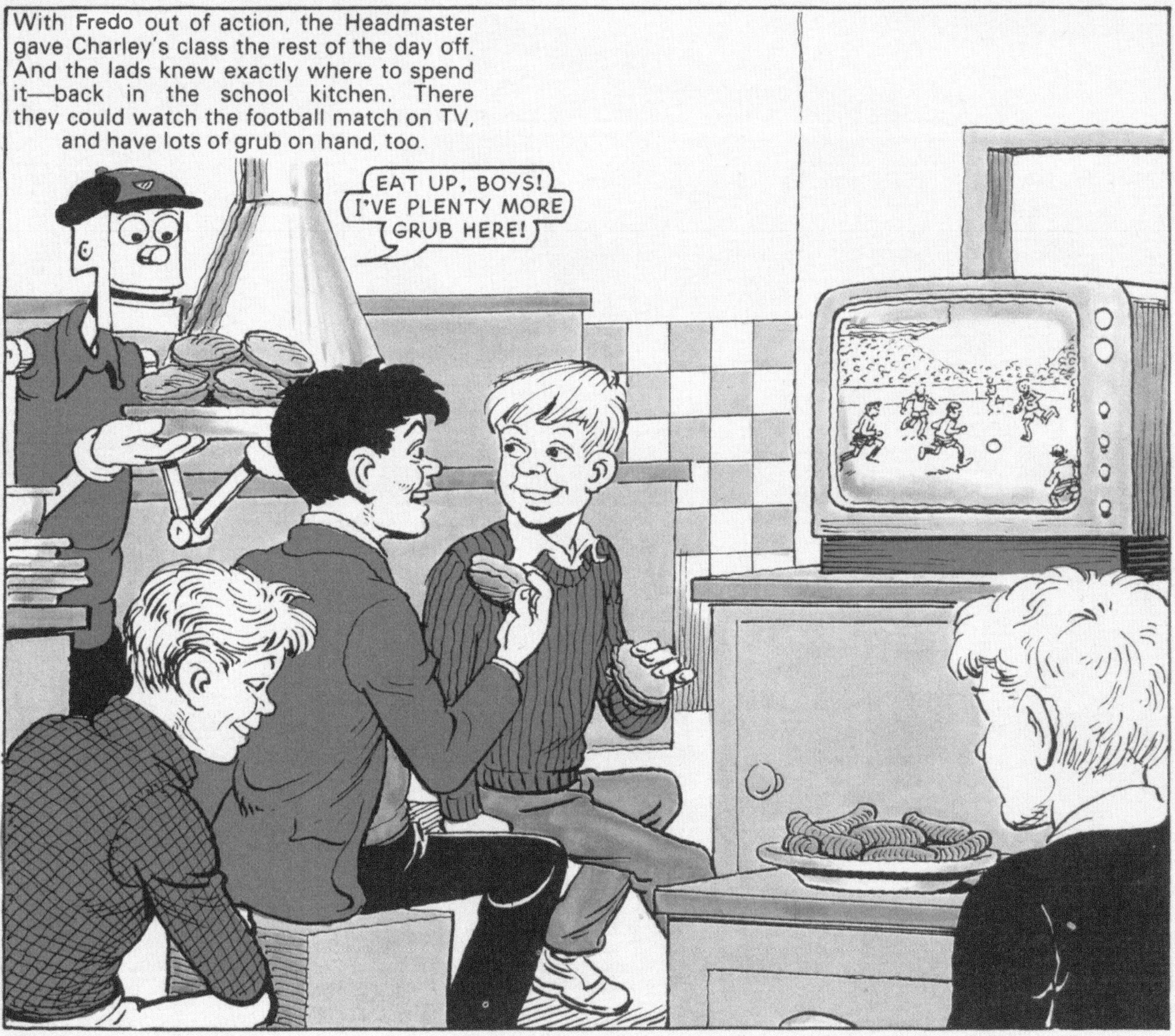

With Fredo out of action, the Headmaster gave Charley's class the rest of the day off. And the lads knew exactly where to spend it—back in the school kitchen. There they could watch the football match on TV, and have lots of grub on hand, too.

EAT UP, BOYS! I'VE PLENTY MORE GRUB HERE!

KORKY the Cat
NO FISHING
HEH-HEH! I COULD GRAB KORKY NOW, BUT I'VE GOT ANOTHER PLAN. THIS RADIO GADGET WILL HELP ME TO KEEP A CHECK ON WHERE KORKY IS ALL THE TIME!
ZZZZZ
FISHING
SO!
NOW, LET ME SEE IF IT WORKS—YES, IT DOES!
BLEEP! BLEEP!
I COULD THROW THE GADGET AWAY, BUT I'VE THOUGHT OF A BETTER IDEA!
A little later, at the village shop—
THERE YOU ARE, KORKY—ONE POT OF HONEY!
HONEY
Later—
BLEEP! BLEEP!
AHA! KORKY'S DOWN AT THE RIVER!
GOT YOU—EEK!
HEE-HEE! I BORROWED THE BEAR FROM MY PAL, THE ZOOKEEPER.
NO FISHING
GRRR
HELP!
GRRR
NOW I CAN FISH IN PEACE!

BERTIE BUNCLE
AND HIS CHEMICAL UNCLE
I'VE JUST INVENTED THIS MIXTURE FOR CHASING AWAY WASPS. GO AND TRY IT OUT IN THE GARDEN, BERTIE.
ALL RIGHT, UNCLE BUNCLE!

THERE'S A WASP! LET ME SEE IF UNCLE BUNCLE'S SPRAY IS AS GOOD AS HE SAYS.

AARGH! UNCLE WAS WRONG! WASPS DON'T HATE IT! IN FACT, THEY SEEM TO LOVE IT!

I SUPPOSE I COULD HAVE GREAT FUN WITH THIS— IF I EVER GET OUT OF HERE!

Later—
THEY WENT AWAY AT LAST, THANK GOODNESS!

HEY! WHAT ARE YOU DOING, BUNCLE?
MAKING YOU BUZZ OFF, THAT'S ALL!

DEAR, DEAR! HE'S RUSHED AWAY AND LEFT ALL HIS SANDWICHES LYING ON THE BENCH!
HELP!

NO POINT IN WASTING GOOD FOOD! SLURP!

MOLLY
PARPLE!
FATHER, I WANT ONE OF THESE AND I WANT IT NOW.
EH? WHAT'S THAT, THEN?
RIGHT... OKAY... A WOOLLY MAMM...
...SWOON.
WHOEVER HEARD OF A WOOLLY MAMM-SWOON? AND THAT'S TYPICAL – SLEEPING WHEN THERE'S WORK TO BE DONE.
WAKE UP, YOU!
GLUB!
YOU WANT A WOOLLY MAMMOTH? WHERE AM I GOING TO GET ONE OF THEM AT THIS TIME OF DAY?
THAT'S YOUR PROBLEM, SUNSHINE.

Soon...
HOW'S THIS?
IT'S A DOPEY-LOOKING NELLYFANT IN A REALLY BAD WIG AND A MUCH WORSE FAKE BEARD. PATHETIC!
PARP!
SCIENCE MUSEUM
HONESTLY, IF YOU WANT SOMETHING DONE...
...YOU HAVE TO DO IT YOURSELF. I MEAN, IT'S NOT THAT MUCH TO ASK FOR – ONE WOOLLY MAMMOTH!
OI, CLONE-BOY! SLING YOUR HOOK, I'VE GOT WORK TO DO.
CLONES R-US
DOH!
RIGHT, WITH BITS OF OLD MAMMOTH BONE, I CAN CLONE UP A MAMMOTH FOR MYSELF. BWAH-HAH-HAH!
YEEKS! THAT'S NIPPING!

WHARY! IT WORKED! WELL, I ALWAYS THOUGHT IT WOULD.
HAPPY PARPLINGS!
ZAP!
ZAP
HANG ON. I CAN'T GET IT TO STOP. TOO MANY CLONE MAMMOTHS! RUN!
RUN? OKAY, WE WILL. HEAD FOR THE FIELDS, GIRLS! PARP!
SHRIEKS! OW! OOH! GERROFF! MIND YOUR FEET! OWCHA!
D.MOSTYN 2003
THAT'S SMART WORK, MOLLY. A WHOLE HERD OF HAIRY HEFFALUMPS!
?
GROAN! MONSTERS. BE A PAL AND CLONE A NEW BODY FOR ME, WOULD YOU? MOAN!

MY HERO
2004
2001
1995
1983
1970
I'VE INVENTED A TIME MACHINE SO I CAN GO BACK AND MEET MY HERO, ALBERT EINSTEIN.
HE'S THE SMARTEST BLOKE EVER. HE'S EVEN SMARTER THAN CAROL VORDERMAN. HI, ALBERT.
BUT HE'S RANK AT COMPUTER GAMES SO I'M SMARTER THAN HIM. WAHEY!
I CAN'T GET MEIN NOODLE AROUND ZIS DOPEY GAME.
BZZZT!
ZAP!
PWEEEE!

RUBI'S SCREWTOP SCIENCE

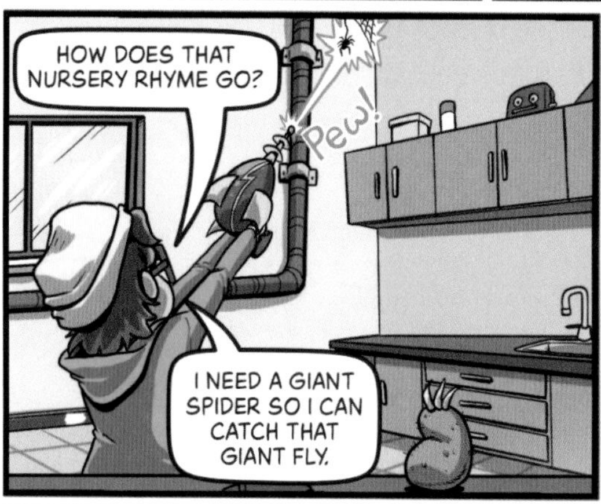

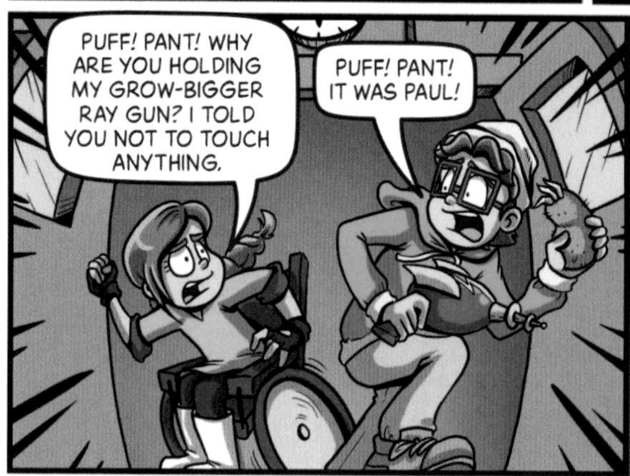

ARRGH! TO CATCH A GIANT SPIDER, WE NEED...
...A GIANT BIRD!
Pew!
NO! WAIT!
HAVE YOU GONE COMPLETELY *CUCKOO?*
CUCKOO? IT LOOKS MORE LIKE A PIGEON TO ME.
GULP
BUT...
SCREECH!
UH-OH! IT STILL LOOKS HUNGRY.
WE ARE IN *BIG* TROUBLE NOW!
TO CATCH A GIANT BIRD, WE NEED A GIANT CAT!
SIGH! I SHOULD REALLY HAVE TAKEN THAT RAY GUN FROM YOU BY NOW.
Pew!
SCREECH!
ROAR!
NICE KITTY-CAT.
GIVE ME THAT BACK!
TO STOP A GIANT CAT, WE NEED...
BITS + BOBS
...A GIANT *BALL OF STRING!*
Pew!
PURR!
THAT SHOULD GIVE ME ENOUGH TIME TO INVENT A GROW-SMALLER RAY GUN.
PHEW! WE'VE AVOIDED A GIANT *CAT-ASTROPHE!*

HAR HAR'S JOKE SHOP!
MEET BEANOTOWN'S FUNNIEST FAMILY!
HARI
SAHANA
HEENA
HARSHA
HANI

SCHOOL IS ABOUT TO BEGIN...
HAVE A TASTE OF THE MEGA MOISTER 500!
NOT IF I BLAST YOU FIRST!
WAAH! STOP THAT IMMEDIATELY!

YOU CAN HAVE THESE BACK AT THE END OF THE DAY!
AWW!

IN CLASS...
LEARN!
HEE-HEE! I LOVE FART CLASS!
FRRRT!
FRAAP!

YOU CAN HAVE THESE BACK AT THE END OF THE DAY!
LEARN!
BOO!

LATER, IN HANI'S CLASS...
I'LL BE CONFISCATING THIS UNTIL THE END OF THE SCHOOL DAY!
SORRY, SIR!

LUNCHTIME...
OLIVE'S EGGS ARE LIKE RUBBER ANYWAY! HA-HA!
YOU CAN HAVE YOUR RUBBER EGGS BACK...
I KNOW, I KNOW... AT THE END OF THE DAY!

AT THE END OF THE DAY...
WELL, SCHOOL'S DONE.
TIME TO RECLAIM OUR PRANKS!

WAIT! WHAT'S ALL THAT LAUGHTER? TEACHERS DON'T LAUGH!
FRRRT!
STAFF ROOM
HEE-HEE!
HA-HA!

GASP!
WAAH! SPIDERS!
TEE-HEE!
CALM AND TEACH
FRAAP!
HA-HA!
TAKE THAT!
HOW TO TEACH

WELL, AT THE END OF THE DAY, WHO CAN RESIST OUR AWESOME PRANKS AND JOKES?

RUBI'S LAUGHTER LAB!
These jokes have been scientifically proven to be funny!
Why are chemists perfect for solving problems? Because they have all the solutions!
What do spacemen do in their spare time? They play astro-nauts and crosses!
How do scientists freshen their breath? With experi-mints!
Why couldn't the astronaut book a hotel room on the moon? It was full!
Why did the germ cross the microscope? To get to the other slide!
I read a book about gravity... ...it was impossible to put down!
What happens when a chemistry joke isn't funny? There's no reaction!

HAR HAR'S JOKE SHOP!
MEET BEANOTOWN'S FUNNIEST FAMILY!
HARI
SAHANA
HEENA
HARSHA
HANI

WHAT ARE YOU DOING?
DAD! HARSHA'S WRITING ALL OVER MY BOOK REPORT THAT I NEED TO PRESENT IN CLASS TODAY!

DON'T PANIC! LOOK!

WHERE DID IT GO?
IT'S DISAPPEARING INK! OOH... MAGIC!

JUST DON'T MESS WITH MY THINGS, OKAY?

WHAT'S WITH ALL THE SHOUTING?
I WAS JUST TRICKING HEENA WITH THE DISAPPEARING INK PEN YOU GAVE ME, DAD.

I GAVE YOU THE PEN BECAUSE IT WAS FAULTY! THE INK REAPPEARS AFTER A COUPLE OF HOURS!

OH NO! THAT MEANS...

A COUPLE OF HOURS LATER AT SCHOOL...
SO, IN CONCLUSION, 'SPACE VAMPIRE ROMANCE' SHOWS US THAT THERE'S GOOD IN US ALL. ALSO, I EAT MY OWN BOGIES AND I HAVE A CRUSH ON TOMMY.

HA-HA-HA!

THAT EVENING...
SNARL! HARSHA! I WANT A WORD!
YIKES! TIME FOR ME TO DISAPPEAR! ARRGH! IT'S NOT WORKING!

RUBI'S
SCREWTOP SCIENCE

THERE HAS BEEN ANOTHER REPORTED SIGHTING OF THE LAKE MESS MONSTER.
WHAT A LOAD OF RUBBISH. THERE'S NO SUCH THING.
IT'S REAL, RUBIDIUM. I HAVE PROOF IT EXISTS.

I MANAGED TO TAKE A PHOTO OF IT ONCE.
THAT COULD BE ANYTHING!

THE LAKE MESS MONSTER IS REAL AND I'M GOING TO PROVE IT!
HOW ARE YOU GOING TO DO THAT?

AT LAKE MESS...
I'M GOING TO FIND THE MONSTER. IT'LL BE THE GREATEST SCIENTIFIC DISCOVERY OF ALL TIME.
LAKE MESS
YOU REALLY WEREN'T KIDDING.

I'VE HIRED US A BOAT SO WE CAN GO OUT ON THE LAKE.
WOW! YOU'VE SPARED NO EXPENSE!

HERE WE ARE!
OH.
BOATY M'BOATFACE

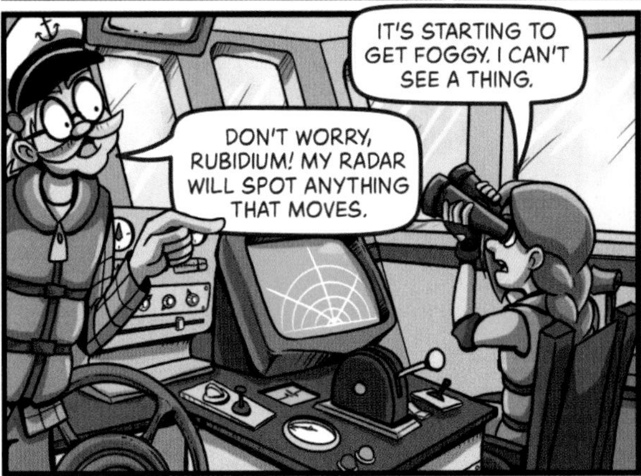
IT'S STARTING TO GET FOGGY. I CAN'T SEE A THING.
DON'T WORRY, RUBIDIUM! MY RADAR WILL SPOT ANYTHING THAT MOVES.

WAKE ME UP WHEN YOU'VE FOUND YOUR MONSTER.
I'LL SHOW YOU!

LATER...
RUBIDIUM! WAKE UP!
SHAKE!
WHAT IS IT?

LOOK ON THE RADAR. THAT'S GOT TO BE THE LAKE MESS MONSTER.

LET'S GO FOR A CLOSER LOOK.
QUACK!
IT'S RIGHT NEXT TO THE BOAT.
WAIT A MINUTE...

HA-HA! YOU'VE MADE A **QUACKING** DISCOVERY HERE, DAD.
OH.
QUACK!
QUACK!

LET ME SEE IF I CAN MAKE A FEW MODIFICATIONS TO YOUR RADAR.

A FEW MODIFICATIONS LATER...
I'VE INCREASED THE RANGE AND ACCURACY.

NOW I CAN PROVE THERE'S NO MONSTER IN THIS LAKE.

I DON'T BELIEVE IT. I THINK I CAN SEE SOMETHING.
BOATY M^cBOATFACE
I TOLD YOU. FULL STEAM AHEAD!
WHOOSH!

IT SHOULD BE RIGHT IN FRONT OF US. IT'S MASSIVE!
WE'RE GOING TO NEED A BIGGER BOAT!

I THINK I CAN SEE IT!
I'M GOING TO WIN ANOTHER NOBEL PRIZE FOR THIS!
TRUMPET!

WAIT A MINUTE. HAND ME THE BINOCULARS.

IT'S THE ELEPHANT THAT KEEPS ESCAPING FROM BEANOTOWN ZOO.
WHAT?!

ELLIS, GET BACK HERE NOW!
SIGH!

SORRY, DAD. THE LAKE MESS MONSTER JUST DOESN'T EXIST. LIKE BIGFOOT OR YETIS.
GULP!

SIGH! I GUESS YOU'RE RIGHT, RUBIDIUM. LET'S GO HOME.
LAKE MESS

THE ORDINARY GIRL WITH THE EXTRAORDINARY BEST FRIEND!

I'M JUST PUTTING THE FINISHING TOUCHES TO THIS SHRINK RAY. THEN I CAN SHRINK AND STORE LOTS MORE BEANOS IN MY ROOM!

CLONK!

ZAP!

OOPS! THAT'S NOT RIGHT!

MEANWHILE...

LET'S GO TO TOYSAURUS. I WANT A NEW ACTION FIGURE.

GRUNT.

SUDDENLY...

ZAP!

OH MY GOODNESS! YOU ARE *SO CUTE!*

WHO NEEDS A NEW ACTION FIGURE? I'M GONNA DRESS YOU UP LIKE A DOLL!

SO...

LOOK! YOU CAN PLAY WITH HAMBURGER THE HAMSTER NOW!

AT RUBI'S...

THWONK!

IF IN DOUBT... ***WHACK IT!***

BUT...

ZAPPP!

OH, YOU'RE BACK TO NORMAL.

TSK! AND I THOUGHT TODAY WAS GOING TO BE DIFFERENT.

DO YOU WANT TO TELL HER ABOUT HAMBURGER OR SHOULD I, READERS?! - ED

HR

NUMSKULLS

The Little guys that Live in your head! Everybody has them!

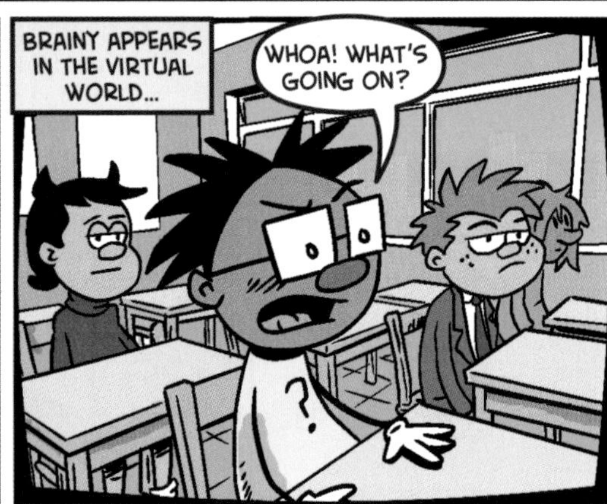

DANGEROUS DAN
BEANOTOWN'S *TOP SPY!*

DAN IS PLAYING 'FORKNITE', BUT...
WHERE IS EVERYONE? THE SERVER'S EMPTY!

IN THE GAME...
THAT'S BECAUSE OF ME, DAN. I HAD TO KICK EVERYONE OFF SO WE COULD TALK IN PRIVATE.
AGENT Q!

IT'S A DARK TIME. S.M.I.R.K.* AND GENERAL BLIGHT HAVE TEAMED UP! ONLY YOU CAN STOP THEM!
WHAT ABOUT BANANAMAN?
BANANAMAN HASN'T BEEN SEEN. NO-ONE KNOWS WHERE HE IS!
*SECRET MINISTRY OF INTELLIGENT ROTTERS KOMMITTEE. - ED

MEANWHILE, ERIC IS GETTING SOME BAD NEWS FROM REG THE VEG...
SORRY, YOUNG ERIC, I'M FRESH OUT OF BANANAS. THE BANANA VAN BROKE DOWN IN DANDYTOWN!

GENERAL BLIGHT OFTEN USES HEAVY EQUIPMENT TO BATTLE BANANAMAN SO THERE'S A LITTLE SOMETHING TO HELP YOU OUTSIDE.

OUTSIDE...
AW YEAH!

NEARBY, THE GENERAL AND THE PREFECT ARE WORKING OUT THE NEW PARTNERSHIP...
YOU DRIVE. I WANT TO OPERATE THE POWERFUL WEAPON!
I CAN'T DRIVE! I'LL HAVE TO OPERATE THE SUPER-POWERFUL WEAPON!
MECHA HOVERCRAFT 2000

NOT SO FAST, PREFECT! AND GENERAL BLIGHT!
DAN! YOU LOOK DIFFERENT. HAVE YOU CHANGED YOUR HAIR?
I'M WEARING A HIGH-TECH BATTLE SUIT!

WHOA! HE'S ROCKETING TOWARDS US AT DRAMATIC SPEED! HE'S GOING SO FAST I'M SURPRISED THAT I HAVE TIME TO SAY ALL THIS!
STOP TALKING! HAND ME THE LASER!
PREFECT
MECHA HOVERCRAFT 3000
GASP! I'VE BEEN SHRUNK!
AND SO HAS MY SUIT!
SO IS THIS LIKE A SHRINK RAY?
NO! IT'S NOT 'LIKE' A SHRINK RAY! IT *IS* A SHRINK RAY!
MECHA HOVERCRAFT 3000
ZAP
BA-ZOINK!
HOW CAN I DEFEAT THEM NOW?
WHAT IF THEY WIN?!

BA-ZOINK!
HUH?
PREFECT
I'LL HIDE BEHIND THIS VAN UNTIL I FIGURE OUT WHAT TO DO!
BA-ZOINK!
HA-HA-HA! YOU'VE NOWHERE TO HIDE WHILE I HAVE THIS SHRINK RAY!
THIS ISN'T FAIR!
I KNOW! I'M LOVING IT!
YOU LOOK DIFFERENT, DAN. HAVE YOU CUT YOUR HAIR?
DAN'S PLAN IS... TO GIVE UP!
HA-HA-HA!
YOU'VE WON! YOU BEAT ME, YOU CAN TAKE OVER THE TOWN AND RULE WITH AN IRON FIST...
...GENERAL!

WHAT?! NO! NOW WE'VE WON, I'M IN CHARGE!

YOU CAN'T RULE THE TOWN WITH AN IRON FIST!
OH, YOU'RE IN CHARGE BECAUSE YOU'RE BIGGER THAN ME? IS THAT IT?
YES!
PREFECT

BA-ZOINK!
HA-HA!

WHO'S BIGGER NOW, GENERAL?!
GASP!
HA-HA-HA!
PREFECT

WE'LL SEE ABOUT THAT!
PREFECT

SHRINK!
BA-ZOINK!

HEY! YOU SHRUNK ME! TAKE THAT!
BA-ZOINK!
ARRGH! I'M DOUBLE SHRUNK! TAKE THAT!
BA-ZOINK!
BA-ZOINK!
BA-ZOINK!
BA-ZOINK!

SEVERAL BA-ZOINKS LATER...
SO MUCH FOR YOUR BIG IDEA, GUYS...
...I SEE A SMALL PROBLEM IN YOUR PLAN!

GNASHER
& GNIPPER
THE ADVENTURES OF
BEANOTOWN'S MENACE HOUNDS!

YOU'LL NEVER GUESS WHAT I'VE BOUGHT!
SAUSAGES?

IT'S A ROBOT DOG!
GNOO-ER!

IT CAN DO BACKFLIPS!
JEALOUS!
JEALOUS!
ANYONE CAN DO THAT!

OOF! MAYBE GNOT!
BEST OF ALL, IT NEVER TRIES TO STEAL MY SAUSAGE SANDWICHES!
BLAT!

THAT CAN'T BE RIGHT! EVERY DOG LOVES SAUSAGES!

HERE! TRY SOME!

IT'S GOING CRAZY!
ZOOM!
IT MUST BE A SAUSAGE RUSH!

TUM-TI-TUM...

...ARRGH!
BLAT!

CRASH!

NOW IT LOOKS LIKE WE'VE GOT A ROBOT DAD!
GNEE-HEE! I WONDER IF HE DOES BACKFLIPS?

Hang up your lab coats, that's all we have for today!

We hope you enjoyed our examination of science and its appliances for our Beano and The Dandy chums. Whether it was kooky professors testing out their madcap potions on our unsuspecting pals or a new-fangled gadget going haywire in spectacular fashion, we proved our hypothesis with our testing sample – these characters are always a test-tube full of fun!

OWL-HOOT JUICE
STEVE BRIGHT